Complete Sonatas Part 1

Recent Researches in Music

A-R Editions publishes seven series of critical editions, spanning the history of Western music, American music, and oral traditions.

Recent Researches in the Music of the Middle Ages and Early Renaissance
Charles M. Atkinson, general editor

Recent Researches in the Music of the Renaissance
James Haar, general editor

Recent Researches in the Music of the Baroque Era
Christoph Wolff, general editor

Recent Researches in the Music of the Classical Era
Eugene K. Wolf, general editor

Recent Researches in the Music of the Nineteenth and Early Twentieth Centuries
Rufus Hallmark, general editor

Recent Researches in American Music
John M. Graziano, general editor

Recent Researches in the Oral Traditions of Music
Philip V. Bohlman, general editor

Each edition in *Recent Researches* is devoted to works by a single composer or to a single genre. The content is chosen for its high quality and historical importance, and each edition includes a substantial introduction and critical report. The music is engraved according to the highest standards of production using the proprietary software MusE, owned by MusicNotes, Inc.

For information on establishing a standing order to any of our series, or for editorial guidelines on submitting proposals, please contact:

A-R Editions, Inc.
Middleton, Wisconsin

800 736-0070 (U.S. book orders)
608 836-9000 (phone)
608 831-8200 (fax)
http://www.areditions.com

Recent Researches in the Music of the Baroque Era, 116

Nicola Francesco Haym

Complete Sonatas Part 1

Edited by Lowell E. Lindgren

A-R Editions, Inc.
Middleton, Wisconsin

To Delores Arline Lindgren and Richard Chester Hoglund

Performance parts are available from the publisher.

A-R Editions, Inc., Middleton, Wisconsin

Printed in the United States of America

ISBN 0-89579-503-5
ISSN 0484-0828

♾ The paper used in this publication meets the minimum requirements of the American National Standard for Information Sciences—Permanence of Paper for Printed Library Materials, ANSI Z39.48-1984.

Contents

Acknowledgments

This edition was made possible by the kind cooperation of many fine librarians, scholars, and co-workers, who supplied both basic and cognate source material and information.

I am very grateful to the librarians who sent source material from their collections, answered queries about their holdings, and gave permission for publication of the music and plates found in this edition. At the Library of Congress, they were Charles Sens, Music Specialist, and Kevin LaVine, Music Reference Librarian. At the British Library, they were John Hopson, Archivist, and Andrew Levett of the Division of Music Reproductions. At the British Museum, it was Martin Royalton-Kisch, Assistant Keeper of Flemish Prints and Drawings. At the National Portrait Gallery in London, it was James Kilvington, Assistant Picture Library Manager. At the Bodleian Library in Oxford, they were Peter Ward-Jones, Music Librarian, and Robert J. Bruce, Associate Music Librarian. At Christ Church Library in Oxford, they were John Milsom, Music Specialist, and Janet McMullin, Assistant Librarian. At the Cardiff University Library, it was Gillian Jones, Music Librarian. At the Bibliothèque du Conservatoire Royal in Brussels, it was Paul Raspé, Librarian. At the library of Count Schönborn in Wiesentheid, it was Frohmut Dangel-Hofmann, Bibliothekarische Betreuerin. At the Deutsches Musikgeschichtliches Archiv in Kassel, it was Rainer Birkendorf. At the Conservatorio di Musica "Giuseppe Verdi" in Milan, it was Agostina Zecca Laterza, Librarian. At the Studio Per Edizioni Scelte (S.P.E.S.) in Florence, it was Paola Barocchi, Director.

The following scholars, who are among my good friends, have graciously supplied much information. In alphabetical order, they are Peter Allsop, Paul Atkin, the late Malcolm Boyd, Michael Burden, Paul Corneilson, Anthony DelDonna, Piero Gargiulo, Elizabeth Gibson, Robert D. Hume, Judith Milhous, Curtis Alexander Price, Rudolf Rasch, and Brent Wissick. Dr. Rasch, who is currently completing a study that focuses on the publishing firm of Estienne Roger, has supplied answers to numerous queries about Haym's only publisher, and I am deeply grateful to him for his steadfast help.

The following "specialists" have been my co-workers on this edition: Jeffrey Morrow, M.I.T. class of 1996, John McKay, M.I.T. class of 2000, Mark Ethier, M.I.T. class of 2001, and Lori Holmes, Boston Conservatory class of 2003. John, my chief collaborator, scored all of part 1 and Haym's op. 2 in part 2. His solutions to notational problems were invariably thoughtful and insightful. Jeffrey scored the cello sonatas in part 2. Mark scored the sonata by Gio. Ant. Haym that ends part 2. Lori made the glossy photographs that served as the basis for six of the eight plates.

Christopher Hogwood, director of the Handel and Haydn Society in Boston, provided the impetus for this edition by asking two questions on 2 May 1999, the final day of a Handel conference that he had sponsored. I had made various comments concerning Haym at sessions of the conference, and Hogwood asked first how much of Haym's instrumental music was in print. I said "none," so he then asked why I had not edited any. The next week I ordered copies of Haym's opp. 1 and 2 from both the Library of Congress and the Bodleian Library, then spoke with John McKay, who was looking for an instructive and wage-earning endeavor for the summer. I trust and hope that you will make these hitherto hidden treasures audible to us all.

Introduction

The Composer's Career, Especially in the Chamber

Nicola Francesco Haym "was born at Rome in the year 1678 on July 6 at 11:15 in the morning, Italian style."[1] His father Sebastiano Haim was born during the Thirty Years War (1618–48) in Füssen, a Bavarian town in the see of Augsburg.[2] He was trained within its well-known tradition of stringed-instrument makers,[3] then built lutes at Rome from 1655, married a Roman named Barbara Turpini on 19 January 1659, had his own shop in the via dei Leutari in 1659–87, and died before 1695.[4] His first son was conceivably Giovanni Antonio Haym (fl. 1680–1729), who performed in Rome as a free-lance cellist, contrabassist, lutenist, archlutenist, and trombonist.[5] Giovanni Antonio featured the archlute in his only known work, which is printed and discussed in part 2 of this edition.

Nicola began his career by "divinely touching the *Violoncello*, or *Four-string Base*."[6] He and his younger brother Pietro Antonio, who worked in Rome as a free-lance violinist and trombonist until his death in 1766, might have studied with Giovanni Antonio, who was presumably their half-brother.[7] Nicola's two cello sonatas—which are printed in part 2—were conjecturally written about 1694 and are his earliest extant compositions. They survive only in a Roman manuscript that also includes a pair of movements attributed to one of his contemporaries, Quirino Colombani.[8] Nicola was known as a professional cellist by 1694,[9] a year during which more than thirty-five musico-dramatic works were produced in Rome.[10] From August 1694 until August 1700, he was paid for playing at eight events sponsored by Cardinal Pietro Ottoboni.[11] The first of them was a dramatic serenata, performed outdoors by three singers and sixty-seven string players. Among the violinists were Arcangelo Corelli, Nicola Cosimi, and Prospero Castrucci. The nine or ten violoncellists and contrabassists were Filippo Amadei, Giovanni Bononcini, Bartolomeo Cimapane, Quirino Colombani, Francesco De Carolis, Giovanni Pietro Franchi, Giovanni Antonio Haym, Nicola Francesco Haym, Francesco Mancini, and presumably Giovanni Lorenzo Lulier, called Giovanni del Violone, the composer of the work.[12]

From 13 September 1695 until 1699, Nicola was an active member of the Accademia di Santa Cecilia, the charitable guild of Roman performers.[13] He presumably earned money by playing for operas, such as *Pirro e Demetrio* (1694) by Alessandro Scarlatti and *La rinovata Camilla* (1698) by Giovanni Bononcini. A decade later, their scores provided the bases for his first two theatrical adaptations in London. Ottoboni was apparently his principal Roman patron. Since the cardinal served as overseer of the Seminario Romano, he may well have recommended Giovanni Antonio and Nicola Francesco Haym for two of its teaching posts. Extant program booklets for the *accademie* presented by students at the seminary during August name Giovanni "for archlute and violoncello" in 1695–99 and list Nicola for "violone" in 1697 and for "archlute and violoncello" in 1699.[14] Ottoboni commissioned two oratorios from Nicola (*David sponsæ restitutus* [1699] and *I dui luminari del Tebro* [1700]),[15] and we can surmise that he also invited Nicola to play chamber music at his residence in the Cancelleria. If so, Nicola presumably played many of Corelli's forty-eight trio sonatas—which had been published at Rome between 1681 and 1694—with their composer, who was the cardinal's music master and lived in the Cancelleria. After Haym's arrival in London, he manifested great esteem for Corelli's trio sonatas by serving as a contributing editor for one complete set and as the sole editor for another.

Haym set forth for England with the Roman violinist Nicola Cosimi on 21 October 1700. Cosimi was about forty years old when he was invited to serve Wriothesley Russell (1680–1711), Marquess of Tavistock and soon-to-be second Duke of Bedford, who had resided at Rome between mid-1698 and mid-1699. The twenty-two-year-old Haym joined him, because Cosimi chose to be accompanied by "his virtuoso companion."[16] The musicians told Cosimi's siblings and Haym's widowed mother that they were making a pilgrimage to Loreto. Thus, both families were scandalized when they learned that their chief wage earners had instead traveled via Paris (where they played several times for the English ambassador, Charles Montagu, Duke of Manchester) to London, where they arrived on 11/22 March 1701.[17]

Bedford had promised each an annual salary of 100 guineas for three years, plus free food and lodging at his residence, Southampton House in Bloomsbury. In return, they organized his private concerts in Bloomsbury and accompanied him during his August through September stays at Bath, Stratton in Hampshire, or Woburn Abbey in Bedfordshire.[18] Cosimi returned to Rome after his fourth year in England, while Haym remained in Bedford's service until the duke died on 26 May 1711. During his fourth through ninth years, which ended on 4 March 1710, Haym was paid fifty guineas annually.[19] In five of the extant receipts, dated October 1703 to October 1708, Haym added "M[aestr]o" after his name, because he served the duke as "Master of his Chamber Musick."[20] According to the anonymous writer of his obituary, he was likewise a master of his instrument, the cello, upon which "he was not equal'd by more than two or three Persons in Europe."[21]

We do not know precisely which works Cosimi and Haym played at their private performances, given at the homes of Bedford and other Englishmen, most notably Charles Calvert, Baron Baltimore.[22] They probably featured the works printed for "violino e violone o cembalo" in Corelli's op. 5 (Rome, 1700) and in Cosimi's *Sonate da camera*, op. 1 (London, 1702). When Cosimi dedicated his twelve sonatas to Bedford on 25 May 1702, he declared that the duke had kindly approved of them at Rome in 1698–99, when they were being written.[23] Charles Burney aptly noted in 1789 that Cosimi was "of Corelli's school, and had seen his opera quinta" and that his sonatas had "considerable merit, for the time."[24] Their "merit" for Cosimi himself is evident in his financial diary: he had only two violin students before their publication, but had twenty afterwards.[25]

The most refined instrumental genre of the day was the trio sonata. In order to perform trios during its first year in England, the duo would have been joined by an English violinist and perhaps by a chord-playing lutenist or harpsichordist. After the Cremonese violinist Gasparo Visconti, called "Gasparini," came to London from Rome during the spring or summer of 1702, he presumably joined the duo for performances of trios.[26] If so, their repertoire presumably included selections from Corelli's opp. 1–4 and from other collections written and published by musicians with whom they had worked in Rome.[27] And they presumably played all the works in two collections published in Amsterdam by Estienne Roger with dedications to the Duke of Bedford: James Sherard's twelve *Sonate a tre*, op. 1 (1701), and Haym's *Dodeci sonate a tre*, op. 1 (1703). Both composers recall—as Cosimi did in 1702—that Bedford had listened appreciatively to their works before they were published.[28] James Sherard (1666–1738) and his elder brother William were primarily botanists. Even though James was "no **profest Musitian**," he hoped "to revive an **Idea** of their [the Italians'] **Great Masters**, and by our faint **Copies**, to put **your Grace** in mind of the excellent **Originalls**." Since James was an amateur violinist, he may well have joined Cosimi and Haym during some of their performances, which may even have included some of his twelve *Sonate a tre*, op. 2.[29] His twenty-four works are all *sonate da chiesa*.

When Haym dedicated his op. 1 to Bedford on 15 February 1703, he declared that the duke, with his "refined understanding of music" (così fina intelligenza della Musica), had "provided strong protection" (qual'appoggio più saldo) for these "first fruits of [his] pen" (questi primi parti della mia penna). Since they were "not found unacceptable to the keen ears of Your Excellency" (mentre non sono stati discari a gl'orecchi di V. E. nel udirli), Haym had "no fear of their nonacceptance by the public" (che non havranno timore di non essere compatiti dal Pubblico). His title page and dedication are elegantly engraved, but his title page pales when compared with those for the first collections by Sherard and Cosimi. Theirs are scenic engravings that include angelic musicians and the dedicatee's shield and motto, "what will be, will be" (che sarà sarà).[30]

Haym's second collection of twelve trio sonatas was gratefully dedicated on 15 October 1704 to Richard Edgcumbe (1680–1758), who had been at Rome in 1697–99, before he became a Member of Parliament for Cornwall, Plympton, and St. Germans. According to Hawkins, Edgcumbe studied with Corelli and commissioned Hugh Howard to paint the composer's portrait.[31] Perhaps he befriended Haym in Rome. But Haym's vague dedication does not tell where, when, or how Edgcumbe provided him with sustenance. We learn only that Haym would consider himself most fortunate if his musical notes could "recompense many obligations" (pagare le tante obligationi), "counterbalance many favors" (contrabilanciar tante grazie), and "erase debts" (satisfaranno i mi debbiti).[32] From their publication in 1703–4 until the last known advertisement for them in 1743, Haym's opp. 1 and 2 each sold for five florins (= guilders) in Amsterdam.[33] This was equivalent to ten shillings in England.

Vocal music was also beloved by Bedford. In 1702, for example, he subsidized at least one theatrical revival of *The Judgment of Paris*, a masque with text by William Congreve and music by John Weldon.[34] Weldon's setting was also revived twice at theatrical concerts of 1704,[35] the year that the annual volume of playhouse songs was dedicated to the duke.[36] Concerts in Southampton House presumably included Italian as well as English vocal music, because in August 1700 the duke had asked Cosimi, who was still in Rome, "to procure 20 or 30 of the best cantatas, some accompanied only by continuo, the others by violins, &c."[37] Most of the Italian cantatas performed at his private concerts were, however, presumably brought to London by the singers. Three Italians whom the duke paid handsomely on 23 May 1702 had conjecturally sung more than once at his home. Fifteen guineas were given to "Signor Walentino," and another fifteen were given to "Signor Carlo [Pietragrua?] and his boy."[38] On 2 June 1704, Haym completed a manuscript containing seven Italian cantatas, all accompanied by violins and continuo, "for the use of the Most Illustrious and Most Excellent Lord, the Duke of Bedford" (per uso del Illus^{mo} et Ecc^{mo} Signore, il Sig^{r} Duca di Bedford's).[39] He also wrote other cantatas, and his obituary notes that "he has left several fine Cantata's behind him."[40]

Commercial Activities

During his first decade in London, Haym could presumably have worked exclusively for the Duke of Bedford. As the "Master of his Chamber Musick," he needed only to organize private concerts, play the cello at them, and compose sonatas and cantatas. However, he became ever more involved with commercial activities, which included performing in public, editing Corelli's opp. 1–5, and organizing theatrical productions. For such productions, he taught singers, edited librettos and scores, and composed chamber music for inter-act entertainment at plays. Since he had come to London as Cosimi's "virtuoso companion," he presumably played with him at most if not all of the private and public concerts listed in the violinist's account book. Cosimi earned £47 by playing at seven public concerts at Lincoln's Inn Fields in 1701–2, then received £30 for performing at five of the ten subscription concerts organized by the singer Katharine Tofts at Lincoln's Inn Fields and Drury Lane in 1703–4.[41] Cosimi, Visconti, and Haym were each given the sumptuous sum of thirty guineas for playing while the King of Spain dined and danced at Windsor on 29–30 December 1703.[42]

In 1703–6, Haym edited Corelli's trio and solo sonatas for his own publisher, Estienne Roger in Amsterdam, and helped to prepare John Walsh's edition of the same trio sonatas. In his advertisement of 25 September 1705, Walsh asserted that "each Opera" in his "new Edition" of Corelli's opp. 1–4 had been "carefully corrected by the Ingenious Signior Nicolini Haiam, who is very well acquainted with the Author and his Works." In the next issue of the same paper, Haym informed "all Lovers of Musick" that he "did not correct the same directly nor indirectly," but had instead "revis'd and corrected the Amsterdam Edition by Stephen Roger, which will be speedily published, and will excel in Beauty and Exactnes[s] any Edition of Correlli's Works hitherto printed." A week later, Walsh invited the public to view affidavits by two witnesses. They declared that Walsh's proofs were "3 months under the said Nicolini Haym's Correction," that they had "at times seen" him "correcting them," and when he "returned the Proofs of the several Operas owned them Correct." Walsh appended a statement by the violinist Gasparini, who revealed that Haym was not Walsh's only editor: "For a further satisfaction to the World of the Exactness of Mr. Walsh's Edition of Corelli's Works, I do also declare to have corrected each Opera of the said Edition, who am well acquainted with the Author and his Works, having been 5 years Corelli's Scholar."[43] In Haym's defense, it should also be noted that Walsh was a shrewd and often unscrupulous businessman, that the two anonymous affidavits were probably from his employees, that Gasparini did not comment on Haym's involvement, and that Haym was respected for his "uncommon Modesty, Candour, Affability and all the amiable Virtues of Life."[44] Yet it seems as if Haym was caught double-dealing—presumably with the hope of doubling his profit—on this occasion.

Haym once again claimed responsibility for Roger's edition in his postscript to the bookseller's advertisement of 18 October 1705: "I acknowledge to have carefully examined this Edition of Corelli's Works and have corrected a multitude of Faults that are in all the former Editions hitherto printed, having had the same above 2 years by me to correct it at leisure. Nicolini Haym." Like Walsh, Roger featured "a Bass doubly printed to the 2d and 4th Opera's," but Roger had "both Basses figured, which is not in any former Edition." Walsh's was "engraven from an exact Score, and printed on Royal Paper," while his rival's was "engraven on Copper from an Italian Score, printed on the best Imperial Paper by Stephen Roger, the like never seen in England before, and carefully corrected by Mr. Haym. This Edition doth excell in Beauty and Exactness all the former Editions of Corelli's Works hitherto printed." Roger's "Books" could be seen at the shops of two booksellers: Francis Vaillant's, "where Subscriptions are taken in," and John Cullen's. This "curious Edition" was "daily expected from Holland" in October 1705.[45] But it may not have been available in London until 3 August 1706, when it culminated an advertisement in *The Post-Man.* Among the twelve items listed, the last four are

> Signior Nicolo Haym's Opera 2, [Carlo Antonio] Marini Opera 7 Consorts [i.e., Sonatas] for Violins and Basses, a new Edition of Corelli's Solo's [op. 5], corrected by Sig. Nicolo Haym, pr. 7s 6d. . . . [and] the new and Genuine Edition of Corelli's Works [opp. 1–4], more correct than any hitherto published, being the only Edition corrected from the Score, by Sig. Nicolo Haym, engraven on Copper and printed on Imperial Paper, pr. £I, 12s 6d.

This advertisement of 1706 provides the only known evidence that Haym was responsible for a new edition of Corelli's op. 5. Rudolf Rasch is aware of three copies of this edition[46] and has compared one of them with the Rome 1700 edition and the Roger 1702 reprint.[47] All three have the same number of pages, the same number of systems per page and—with some exceptions—the same measures on each system. Since the original edition is excellent, the only change that Haym seems to have made is in the *mostra* that ends each staff. Only in his edition is it preceded by an accidental when it prefigures a note with an accidental. Haym had already employed this practice in his opp. 1–2 of 1703–4 and his edition of Corelli's opp. 1–4 of 1705.

Beginning in 1705, Haym became intricately involved with theatrical productions. In that year, both Maria Margherita Gallia, who had been "taught by Signior Nicolini Haym,"[48] and Joanna Maria, Baroness Linchenham (sometimes wrongly spelled Lindelheim), who was known as Haym's "scholar," began their theatrical careers. He managed operatic engagements for his "scholar" between 1705 and 1711, when they lived together on Bow Street, one block from the Drury Lane Theatre. The first was in spring 1705, when he "made a verbal bargaine for his Scholler," who was to receive one hundred guineas from John Vanbrugh and William Congreve for ten performances at their new theater in the Haymarket.[49]

On 14 January 1706, Haym signed "Articles of Agreement" with Christopher Rich concerning the production of his arrangement of Bononcini's *Camilla* at the theater in Drury Lane. In return for £100, Haym supplied an English score and agreed "to play his part on ye Bass

Violl att all times when ye said Opera shall be performed . . . [until] the End of May next." He furthermore agreed to "performe his part if requested in any Subscription Musick [i.e., concert series] or other Extraordinary Musick" at either of Rich's theaters until the end of June. And he promised "to performe three dayes for Mr Rich in every Week" and "to provide some peices [*sic*] of Italian Musick, Aires & Sonata's of best Masters, to be performed . . . by . . . Mr Hyam, Signior Gasperini and others of Mr Rich his Band of Musick" on play-nights, usually as inter-act entertainments. Rich permitted him to "Play in any Private Consort in a Room as he did ye Last Yeare (or he may accompany Signiora Johanna Maria his Schollar in Case she shall sing att ye other house)." He could likewise play at the "other house," i.e., the Queen's Theatre in the Haymarket, "if his Grace ye Duke of Bedford Command him to Play there in the Subscription Musick."[50]

This operatic contract surprisingly reveals much about the great role that chamber music had in Haym's career. In addition to playing at public and private concerts, he provided "Aires & Sonata's" by the "best [Italian] Masters" for play-nights at Drury Lane. Perhaps the first night organized by him was 29 January 1706, when "several Entertainments of Singing in Italian" were provided by Signora Louvicina, "accompanied by Signior Haym, Signior Saggioni, Signior Gasperini, and others, who will perform several Airs and Italian Sonatas never yet perform'd on the English Stage."[51] In February, two evenings included "several Italian Sonatas (between the Acts) by the best Masters."[52] A "Master" is finally named for the night of April 3: "a new Solo never yet perform'd, compos'd by Signior Haym's, and perform'd on the Stage by him and Signior Gasperini."[53] This is the only known reference to an instrumental solo written by Haym for performance on a play-night. He might, however, have written some of those printed at the end of this volume for such occasions.

Haym's arrangement of Bononcini's *Camilla* was the most successful production of its time, in that it received sixty-three performances in 1706–9, then forty-eight more—which were directed by Christopher Pepusch rather than Haym—in 1717–19 and 1726–28. Haym and his "scholar," Baroness Linchenham, were each to receive £300 from Christopher Rich for supplying and performing in his next adaptation, Scarlatti's *Pyrrhus and Demetrius*. Before its production was underway, however, an order from the Lord Chamberlain moved all operas from Drury Lane to the Haymarket Theatre. Haym thus needed a new contract, for which he submitted an impressive list of "pretentions" on 12 January 1708:

> That every time I play at the opera, I be payd two Guineas, and every time I make a new opera, that I have a seperate [*sic*] bargain for it. . . . That I have a power to com[m]and all the [instrumental] Musick. . . . I humbly desire . . . that I be not considered Less, or made Second to any other person of ye Musick, neither as to ye profit; nor any other Matter, beli[e]ving my self perhaps, not of inferiour merit to any of my Profession now in England—particular[l]y of ye foreigners.[54]

The Venetian painter Marco Ricci, who arrived at London in autumn 1708, depicted two rehearsals of *Pyrrhus and Demetrius*. In one of them, Nicola Grimaldi (Pyrrhus) and Katharine Tofts (Climene) are singing a duet, while Margarita del L'Épine (Marius) and Baroness Linchenham (Deidamia) stand in the background. The accompanists include two violinists, a violist, and a bespectacled, bewigged, heavy-set cellist, who is leaning far to the left (because of bad eyesight?) in order to read the score placed in front of the harpsichordist. Only the toes of this cellist's left foot seem to touch the floor, and his precarious position makes it clear that he could not "command all the Musick."[55] In the second painting (see plate 1), the cellist is youthful and lithe, and his hair is covered by a jockey's cap. He is presumably the thirty-year-old adapter of the opera, for he seems to have stopped the rehearsal in order to make a point. His left hand points at the score while Grimaldi points imperiously at him. Meanwhile, the harpsichordist, the double bassist, and even one of the dogs stare at him. A woman seated at the foot of the harpsichord, who is looking at Grimaldi, may well be the Baroness.[56] The landscape painting on the rear wall seems to represent Mount Edgcumbe, the home of Richard Edgcumbe, dedicatee of Haym's op. 2.[57] The accuracy of Ricci's depictions of the number and location of continuo cellists is confirmed by an orchestral list of 1710, which specifies: "Heyam & Pilotti to play every night and to take their places att ye Harpiscord [*sic*] by Turns."[58]

Pyrrhus and Demetrius, given fifty-nine times between 1708 and 1717, was the second most successful opera produced in early-eighteenth-century London. It and *Camilla* are the only works lauded in "A Critical Discourse on Opera's and Musick in England" (1709).[59] They show that Haym adjusted exceptionally well to rapidly changing conditions in London. When he edited Bononcini's *Camilla* in 1705–6, he retained the original overture and aria settings, and the production was spectacularly successful. When he reworked *Pyrrhus and Demetrius* in 1707–8, he had to accommodate the demands of newly arrived Italian "stars" and a far more experienced audience. As a result, he composed the overture and twenty-one arias himself, inserted nineteen "suitcase arias" (mainly for the two castratos, who presumably brought most of them to London), and retained only fourteen of Scarlatti's original aria settings.

Literary Endeavors

The premiere of Handel's first opera written for the London stage and the death of Bedford were two events of 1711 that significantly changed the path of Haym's career. In order to earn money, he henceforth organized public concerts, served the Earl of Carnarvon as a musician, and worked at the opera house until his death. His subsequent work with operas focused on text editing, which complemented his other literary endeavors. In a pair of volumes concerning ancient coins, he manifested his knowledge of ancient history, his ready access to the collections of British lords, and his skill as an engraver.

In three later volumes, he demonstrated his literary scholarship, and in a pair of volumes that are—alas—lost, he conveyed his understanding of the history of music.

During the spring seasons of 1712–17, Haym shared in the sponsorship of eight concerts and single-handedly mounted nine. Although no programs survive for any of them, many of his trio sonatas, solo sonatas, Italian cantatas, and opera arias were presumably performed.[60] In 1712, Thomas Clayton, Charles Dieupart, and Haym managed a subscription series of eight concerts and explained their goals in two letters to *The Spectator.*[61] Haym's own series of five in 1713 was strongly recommended by "Nestor Ironside" (i.e., Richard Steele) in *The Guardian:* "I have frequently taken great Satisfaction in hearing the Composures of *Nicolino Haym,* a Man of great Merit and Skill in his Profession, accompanied with so much Modesty, that he loses the Force which our Affectation of Foreigners might have towards his Advancement, and is, by his Deference and Respect to us, under the same Disadvantage as if he were born among us."[62] Between 1714 and 1717, Haym organized one concert each spring for the benefit of Baroness Linchenham, with whom he lived on Bridges Street, Covent Garden.[63] A well-known Italian violinist appeared at each benefit: Francesco Maria Veracini in 1714, Alessandro Bitti in 1715 and 1717, and Pietro or Prospero Castrucci in 1716.[64] If two good violinists played at each concert, some of Haym's trio sonatas may well have been on the program. During his lifetime, only one documented performance of any of his trio sonatas is known: on 11 November 1714, an Oxford music club heard "Dr.[!] Haim's 7 first sonatas."[65]

After Bedford's death in 1711, Haym received an annual stipend from Charles Montague, Baron Halifax, which gave him time to work on his study of ancient medals. After Halifax died in May 1715, Haym was employed as a musician at the Cannons estate of James Brydges, Earl of Carnarvon (later Duke of Chandos) until at least September 1718. His annual salary of £50 was higher than that of any other musician at Cannons,[66] so he presumably served as continuo cellist and composer. Five of the six anthems that he wrote for Carnarvon's chapel in 1716 begin with a sinfonia in trio texture, and the instruments play ritornelli between the verses of each psalm setting.[67] Haym completed his study of medals while working for Carnarvon, and he dedicated volume 1 of the published version to his patron.

Haym's involvement with operas remained the same after the production of *Pyrrhus and Demetrius* in that he was still employed as a cellist or continuo cellist whenever his managerial duties—which included stage directing—did not keep him from playing in the orchestra. From 1710 onwards, he mainly revised libretti in order to incorporate whatever "suitcase" arias the newly arrived singers had brought with them. He took on such responsibilities for at least four and perhaps as many as eight *pasticci* of 1710–17.[68] For Handel, he definitely revised the French libretto of *Teseo* (1713), and he may have also reworked the Italian predecessors for *Amadigi* (1715) and *Radamisto* (1720). For Ariosti he may have created a new work called *Tito Manlio* (1717), because no predecessor for it is known, and it—like all of his adaptations—shrewdly minimizes the amount of story telling in simple recitatives, which must have bored the English. Instead, it stresses melodramatic incidents that call for accompanied recitatives and culminate with abjectly languorous or thrillingly heroic arias.

In a plan of 15 February 1720 for the new Royal Academy of Music, Haym is listed as one of the two principal cellists.[69] But in 1722 he succeeded Paolo Antonio Rolli as secretary to the Royal Academy, "in which Employment he distinguish'd himself by his indefatigable Industry and the general Satisfaction he gave to all the Directors."[70] The academy survived for six more seasons, which were in every way its most glorious. As its secretary, Haym served as the stage manager for twenty-four new productions, at least twelve of which were based upon his adaptations of Italian libretti. Seven were for Handel (*Ottone, Flavio, Giulio Cesare in Egitto, Tamerlano, Rodelinda, Siroe,* and *Tolomeo*), three for Ariosti (*Caio Marzio Coriolano, Vespasiano,* and *Artaserse*), and two for Bononcini (*Calfurnia* and *Astianatte*). Haym may also have done five more for Ariosti (*Aquilio consolo, Dario, Elisa, Lucio Vero,* and *Teuzzone*) as well as one *pasticcio* for Handel (*Elpidia*). His "dramatic skeletons"[71] provided composers and performers with ample space for the display of their art and artifice. Because of his sensible editing, his texts remain eminently stage-worthy today.[72]

Haym "devoted several Hours daily to the *Belles-Lettres,* in which he had made a very great Progress; not to mention his Skill in the learned Languages."[73] Such diligence made him a "Renaissance man," with a comprehensive knowledge not only of music, but also of history, the visual arts, and literature. His first published comments are the anonymous notes in an anonymous translation of [François Raguenet,] *A Comparison between the French and Italian Musick and Opera's* (London, 1709). Since the annotator was intimately familiar with opera in Rome during the late 1600s, he must have been Haym.[74] In 1716, he invited subscriptions for *Del tesoro britannico* (London, 1719–20), which included 780 medals, "all accurately and carefully Engraven on Copper Plates by the Author himself and Illustrated throughout with Explications and Observations on the several Antiquities contained in it."[75] He became so deeply immersed in his work on them that he even had a live specimen of the squirrel-like animal shown on one medal sent from Egypt, so that he could depict it accurately.[76] The mastery exhibited in *The British Treasury* led to Haym's election to the Society of Antiquaries on 9 December 1724.[77]

Haym's three volumes of literary scholarship were published between 1721 and 1726. The first was his edition of two recent tragedies, *La Merope* by Scipione Maffei and *La Demodice* by Giovanni Battista Recanati.[78] The next was his 1724 edition of Torquato Tasso's *La Gierusalemme liberata,* which he dedicated to George I. It contains twenty plates, each of which is dedicated to a different British nobleman.[79] His final and by far most influential literary work was his annotated bibliography, *Notizia de' libri rari nella lingua italiana divisa in quattro parti principali, cioè, istoria, poesia, prose, arti e scienze* (1726). Five revised editions were printed in Italy between 1728 and 1803 with the title *Biblioteca italiana*.[80]

Haym's career ended with antiquarian endeavors in the realm of music. When the Academy of Vocal Musick was formed in 1726–27, he was among its founders and served as its secretary. His final composition, an anthem dated 1728, may well have been written for performance at one of its meetings.[81] He began planning *A General History of Musick* by inviting subscriptions for it in June 1726.[82] By April 1729 he had finished both the Italian text—which was being translated by John Lockman—and the engravings for most of the plates, which included twenty depictions of musical instruments for volume 1 (which covered antiquity to 1550) and sixty "heads" for volume 2 (1550–1729).[83] The writer of his obituary asserted that these volumes, "which Providence just indulg'd him Time to finish, will be a lasting Monument."[84] At present, however, the only known remnants of this project are engravings of three "heads." "N. Haym delin." is at the lower left, and "G[erard] Van der Gucht fecit Aqua" is at the lower right of the engraving that represents "Tomaso Tallis Inglese Compositore" and "Guglielmo Bird Inglese Compositore."[85] Are they based on nothing more than Haym's vivid imagination of how such Renaissance masters might have appeared? Since an identical frame is utilized for a "head" of "Francesca Cuzzoni Sandoni da Parma," it was conjecturally drawn and engraved for Haym's history.[86] If Haym's text is someday found, some of the most fascinating comments should be in Books IV–VII of volume 2. They spanned 1650–1729 and—according to his plan—discussed "the introduction of operas and other kinds of [Italian] music into different parts of Europe," especially England, then gave "some account of the principal masters now living, and the present state of music in all parts of Europe."[87]

John Hawkins had access to a "printed copy of the proposals and plan" for Haym's *General History of Musick*.[88] It included "a list of subscribers in his own hand-writing, scarce amounting to forty in number." On this basis, Hawkins (who was not aware that Haym had died in 1729 or that a translation of his *General History* was then in progress) concluded: "For this reason he dropped the design, and, abandoning the profession of music, betook himself to another, viz., that of a collector of pictures; and in that capacity was employed by Sir Richard [i.e., Robert] Walpole, Dr. [Richard] Mead, and other persons." Haym's employment "in that capacity" had begun by 1709, when Bedford paid him for eight prints.[89] During the next twenty years, he presumably bought from and sold to art-lovers like Walpole and Mead in order to assemble a collection that ultimately included between ten and twenty thousand fine drawings, etchings, and engravings. Some of them are identifiable by his stamped monogram, NH.[90] His art collection—consisting of ancient medals, statues and stones, Renaissance and Baroque prints, musical instruments, and furniture—was grouped into 413 items and sold on six nights, 2–6 March 1730.[91] His 1380 books, twenty-six musical scores, and two musical instruments were sold on nine nights, 9–18 March 1730.[92] These two sale catalogs reveal the immense scope of his collections.

Haym had left Rome together with Cosimi on 21 October 1700, which was an unhappy time for Roman musicians, because the pope had demolished one theater in 1697, had tried to suppress all carnival festivities in 1698–99, and had successfully suppressed them during the holy year of 1700. Ten days after the duo left Rome, Charles II of Spain died, which led to the drawn-out War of the Spanish Succession (1701–14). It, together with earthquakes and other natural disasters, subsequently rendered life in Rome increasingly difficult for musicians.[93] Haym was thus wise to have left Rome and fortunate to have settled in London, where he was encouraged to develop his excellent abilities. He performed and composed chamber music, played a vital role in the first two decades of London's operatic productions, published scholarly books, engraved the plates for at least a pair of them, and was a discerning collector of books and visual artworks. He was a true gentleman, and his

> great Abilities, heighten'd by an uncommon Modesty, Candour, Affability and all the amiable Virtues of Life, make all his Friends sincerely regret his Loss. He was, by his own Desire, privately interr'd in *St. Ann's, Westminster;* the Aversion he had always shewn to Pomp and Ostentation accompanying him to the Grave.[94]

Corelli's Contours, Which Haym Adopted and Adapted

As we have noted, the sixteen-year-old Haym began his career as a free-lance cellist at Rome in 1694. His principal patron was probably Cardinal Pietro Ottoboni, the vice-chancellor of the Church, at whose residence Arcangelo Corelli lived. Since Corelli's forty-eight trio sonatas in opp. 1–4 were published at Rome between 1681 and 1694, it seems likely that Haym played many of them—perhaps even with Corelli and Cosimi—before he and Cosimi left Rome in 1700. If they played Corelli's opp. 1 and 3, which are *sonate da chiesa*, they were presumably joined by an organist or an archlutenist—such as Giovanni Antonio Haym. In one of the notes that Haym added anonymously to *A Comparison between the French and Italian Musick and Operas* (1709), he described Corelli as an impassioned performer.[95] Many other composers had published trio sonatas before 1700 in Rome, Bologna, Venice, etc.[96] Haym asserted that Corelli surpassed all others:

> For the Symphonies [i.e., sonatas], we may boldly say *Corelli* has set a Pattern to all the World, there being not one of his that is Printed but what is Excellent in its kind. After him may be mention'd *Baldassini, Torelli, Bassani* and *Albinoni,* &c.[97]

Haym's "calling cards" for his entrance into the erudite world of composers were his twenty-four trio sonatas, opp. 1–2 of 1703–4, and his four solo sonatas in

VI Sonate da camera of 1710. Opp. 1–2 inevitably manifest Corellian features, because he finished them while he was editing Corelli's opp. 1–4 for his publisher, Estienne Roger. In 1705, he not only completed his editions of Corelli's opp. 1–4 and 5 (the solo sonatas) for Roger, but also helped—like Gasparo Visconti and presumably others—to correct errors in John Walsh's rival publication of Corelli's opp. 1–4. In 1706, Haym's operatic contract specified that he was to supply sonatas by the "best Masters" for performances on play-nights. His four solos in *VI Sonate da camera* might have been written for such nights at Drury Lane in 1706 or 1707.[98] Even though he may well have written new sonatas for the concerts he sponsored in 1712–17, no extant sonata that can be dated after 1710 is attributed to him. His opp. 1–2 and the *VI Sonate da camera* were sold by London booksellers until at least 1726.[99] The *VI Sonate* were also sold, at least in 1734, by LeClerc in Paris.[100] All three publications were sold until at least 1743 in Amsterdam by the firm of Roger and his successors Le Cène and Emanuel-Jean de La Coste,[101] and in The Hague by Nicolas Selhof until his death in 1758.[102] When Le Cène died in April 1743, his stock included twelve copies of Haym's op. 1, eight of his op. 2, and eighteen of the *VI Sonate*. The plates for the latter two publications had already been destroyed or reused. Those for op. 1 weighed fifty-four Dutch pounds and included sixteen full plates and four half plates, which could accommodate up to seventy-two engraved pages (16 × 4 and 4 × 2). This number suits op. 1, which includes sixty-nine engraved pages (title page, dedication, twenty-three in the violin 1 partbook and twenty-two in each of the other two). In 1743, Pietro Antonio Locatelli and Gerhard Fredrik Witvogel determined the worth of the plates and copies of op. 1 to be 22 guilders (= 22 florins) and 4 stuivers, which was equivalent in Britain to 2 pounds, 4 shillings, and 5 pence.[103]

Around 1700, a Roman "calling card" was greatly favored by English chamber musicians, since—according to Roger North—Corelli's op. 1 had "cleared the ground of all other sorts of musick whatsoever. By degrees the rest of his consorts [that is, sonatas], and at last the conciertos [op. 6 of 1714] came, all which are to the musitians like the bread of life."[104] The preeminence bestowed upon Corelli presumably explains why Hawkins and Burney compare Bedford's trio of composers only with him. Although James Sherard never went to Rome, he did note in his dedication to the Duke of Bedford that "by my Brother's attendance on **your Grace** abroad [i.e., at Rome in 1697–98], I was furnish'd with Books, and other Materialls, which gave me the first tast[e] and acquaintance with the *Italian Musick*." Although Sherard does not name a specific model, Hawkins in 1776 labeled his works unmistakably Corellian: "An Englishman, named James Sherard, an apothecary by profession, composed two operas of Sonatas, which an ordinary judge, not knowing that they were the work of another, might mistake for compositions of this great master."[105] Cosimi composed his solo sonatas while Bedford was in Rome. As noted above, Charles Burney judged that they "have considerable merit, for the time," and that Cosimi "was of Corelli's school."[106] Burney wrote also the first evaluation of Haym's sonatas: "He had not only knowledge in counterpoint, but genius for composition, as he published at Amsterdam in 1713 [i.e., 1703–4], two sets of sonatas for two violins and a bass, which are little inferior to the sonatas of Corelli. There is more variety in them, though less grace."[107]

Recent evaluations of Haym's sonatas include four brief commentaries on his trios, but none on his solos.[108] The commentary given in Tilmouth's dissertation of 1959 approves of Haym's imitative writing in op. 1, no. 4, and then praises his idiomatic writing for the violoncello in op. 2, nos. 10–11.[109] In my article of 1987, I stressed the closeness of Haym's relationship to Corelli, declared that his "fondness for imitative counterpoint, which pervades almost every movement, in no way limits the range of affects" in his eleven *sonate da chiesa,* then observed that even more variety in instrumentation, form, and texture is found in his thirteen *sonate da camera*.[110] In a study of 1995, Angela Lepore listed the tempo, meter, key, and number of measures for every movement of all the trio sonatas found in eighteen Roman collections, two of which are by Haym. She noted that the many three-voiced fugal passages in op. 1 are usually found in the second of four movements (i.e., in the usual place for Roman *sonate da chiesa*). She also noted that the two treble parts in op. 1 rarely begin chordally, but frequently begin in canonic imitation. She did not comment on the style of op. 2.[111]

The most recent evaluation is Peter Allsop's of 1999. Even though Haym was a cellist rather than a violinist, Allsop would presumably include him among

> the disciples of Corelli who with evangelistic zeal set out to promulgate his gospel. . . . Their task was greatly facilitated by the phenomenal growth of public concerts—especially in England, where any self-respecting virtuoso would normally include Corelli's Op. 5 along with his own music in his programmes—at least if he wished to stand a hope of success. This gave rise to a mass migration of musicians, particularly from Rome, as Corelli's pupils began to capitalize on this gainful employment. The recent advances in music printing allowed publishers such as Roger in Amsterdam and Walsh in London to produce fine editions at a much-reduced cost which were then circulated widely, and this ensured that Corelli's works (ever the most popular) remained permanently in print.[112]

Allsop cites many differences between the sonatas of Corelli (b. 1653) and Carlo Mannelli (b. 1640), who was displaced by Corelli in 1682 as the principal violinist for the church of San Luigi.[113] Younger contemporaries followed the new leader. Antonio Luigi Baldassini's collections of 1691 and 1699 "already fall into the category of almost slavish imitation," while Giovanni Ravenscroft's opus of 1695 positions him among the "sedulous disciples."[114]

Allsop terms Haym's sonatas of 1703–4

> the exportable deeply derivative commodity to which Hawkins later objected. Even the division of each set into six free sonatas and six *sonate da camera* has Corellian

> overtones. . . . The contents of each sonata are equally circumscribed—Corellian slow introduction, a fugue of distinctly Roman cast, slow tripla, and either a loosely fugal or a dance-like finale, the latter often in dance-like form. . . . These compositions are proficient and not ineffective, but are nevertheless formulaic adaptations of the model.[115]

Allsop's example is Haym's op. 2, no. 1. It borrows "Corelli's much-mentioned 'leap-frogging' effect" in its first and third movements. It resembles Corelli's op. 3, no. 6, and op. 1, no. 11, in its "tightly worked 'canzone' in the serious Roman style." And it "bears more than a passing similarity to the Allegro finale of Corelli's Op. 6 No. 2" in its gavotta finale.[116]

Allsop's observations are surely valid, because Haym himself noted in 1709 that Corelli's excellent sonatas had "set a Pattern to all the World." Haym's opp. 1–2 of 1703–4 are, however, more modern than Corelli's opp. 1–4 of 1681–94. For example, Corelli's are clearly based on the system of eight modes. Therefore, only seven finals utilized in his opp. 1 and 3 have "key" signatures that do not differ from today's practice, while seven have one or two accidentals less than the number required by tonal practice.[117] Haym was apparently far more tonal in outlook, because only two minor-mode signatures in his op. 1 lack an accidental.[118] But the keys in Haym's collection are in the tradition established by Corelli's op. 1, which includes the ten major and minor "keys" from two flats through two sharps, plus A major and C minor. Two who precisely followed the Corellian tradition in their own op. 1 are Boccaletti (1692) and Ravenscroft (1695). Haym's op. 1 differs only in that it supplants the B-minor sonata with a second piece in G major.

The structures found in Haym's sonatas are likewise more up-to-date than those found in Corelli's volumes. In Haym's fugues or canzonas of "distinctly Roman cast," the episodes are far more extensive and are far more often based on clearly contrasting material. In the first exposition of every one of his fugues or canzonas, the continuo is the last part to enter, yet during the course of the movement the subject is usually played more times in the continuo than in either of the treble parts. This might reflect Haym's determination to be in the "driver's seat" when playing the continuo part. His binary forms are more modern in that the second half often consists of a development followed by a recapitulation. Yet in each slow movement, as well as in each half of a binary form, Haym typically progresses from a first to a second motive, then to a third, without stressing any one of them or clearly uniting them by means of a shared motive. In this respect, he is old-fashioned, since he—like Renaissance composers—"taketh a point [= a motive] at his pleasure and wresteth and turneth it as he list, making either much or little of it according as shall seem best in his own conceit."[119] By means of his spinning-out technique, Haym avoids "fastidious" repetition and provides "variety enough," features that were highly prized by his contemporary, Roger North.[120]

Haym's op. 1 is written for two violins and a figured bass intended—according to the title page—for "violone" or "cembalo."[121] This is the precise scoring of Corelli's opp. 2 and 4, both of which contain nothing but *sonate da camera*.[122] They thus feature dance movements in binary form, similar to those found in Haym's op. 1, nos. 7–12, and op. 2, nos. 6–12. Corelli's opp. 1 and 3 were supplied with two bass parts, one labeled "violone" or "arcileuto" and one labeled "organo."[123] The sonatas within them, which feature through-composed movements and motet-like textures, have usually been labeled church sonatas or *sonate da chiesa*. According to Allsop, Corelli wrote them primarily for performance in princely homes, which was clearly the destination of Haym's similar works in op. 1, nos. 1–6, and op. 2, nos. 1–5. Allsop calls them "free sonatas,"[124] a name that seems even better suited to Haym than to Corelli, so it has been adopted in this edition. In Haym's age, they were, however, simply called "by the name of Sonatas," while chamber sonatas in England were called "by the Name of Airs,"[125] which has also been adopted in this edition.

The "Free Sonatas," or *Sonate da chiesa*, in Op. 1, Nos. 1–6

The slow first movements contain thirteen to thirty-five through-composed measures with a contrapuntal texture. Their counterpoint consists either of three-part imitation (nos. 1–2), two-part imitation over a melodic bass (no. 4), or chain suspensions over a walking bass. Such suspensions begin either at the outset (no. 3) or after a motive featuring the bass has been stated and sequenced up a fifth (nos. 5–6). Three movements (nos. 3–4 and 6) underscore "the end" by echoing the closing phrase before they cadence in the tonic. The most affective of them is obviously no. 4, a saraband-like Grave in C minor, in which the closing echo is unexpectedly followed by another outburst of grief. All except no. 4 are in common time, and in them the closing cadence in the tonic is followed by a three-chord transition to the dominant, which—in spite of the ensuing rests and/or fermata—presumably means that movement two should follow *subito*.

The fugal second movements consist of thirty-five to forty-seven through-composed measures in common time.[126] In collections of Roman trio sonatas, the traditional title for this foremost display of contrapuntal skill was "canzone" or "canzona."[127] The Vivace in Haym's no. 1 has a clearly balanced structure, in that each instrument plays the eight-note subject in each six-measure exposition (mm. 1, 11, 21, 31, and 40), then plays other material in the intervening four-measure episodes (mm. 7, 16, 27, and 36). Each exposition ends with a vii$^{\circ 6}$–i cadence, and the final one is "confirmed" by three chords marked Adagio: vii$^{\circ 7}$/V–V^{43}–i. Since the violone (which Haym played) "robs" violin 2 of its subject entries in expositions two and five, it plays seven entries, while the first and second violins play five and three, respectively.

The Andante in no. 3 has two nine-note motives, one in its expositions (mm. 1, 9, 17, 22, and 31) and the other in its episodes (mm. 7, 15, 22, and 31). Both of them feature flowing eighth notes, which provide rhythmic drive, partly by veering away immediately from the V–i cadences that end each exposition. The first two episodes are overlapped by the beginnings of the ensuing expositions after only two measures, and the next two are overlapped *subito*. The only upward leap is the fifth or fourth that begins each exposition. Its fifth and final statement climaxes with the violins' leapfrogging imitation of this upward leap, which results in a chain of suspensions over a walking bass (mm. 34–37). The echoed close is broken apart by hockets.

The Andante[128] in no. 5 is constructed rather "academically." Its subject and three countersubjects each consist of a measure-long motive that is immediately sequenced upward twice or thrice by step. In the first exposition (mm. 1–14), the rhythmically syncopated subject interacts with the first countersubject in a hocket-like manner. The syncopated second countersubject (violin 1 in mm. 6–10 and violin 2 in mm. 10–14) fills in the one silent eighth with two sixteenths. Then the interactive first is replaced by the third countersubject (violin 1 in mm. 10–14), which imitates the subject's rhythm (three eighths plus a quarter). Such hocketing and imitation, as well as the sixteenth notes in the medial episode (mm. 15–18), provide great rhythmic drive. The climax is reached in the final exposition (m. 36), when violin 2 stresses the highest pitch in the movement (the tritone above the tonic), just before the return from the dominant to the tonic key.

The second movements in even-numbered sonatas have no episodic material between their expositions, but each evokes a distinctly different affective character. The sprightliest is no. 6. Its eleven-note, vivace subject is played eleven times: thrice in stretto (m. 1), once by the violone (m. 10), thrice in stretto (m. 17), once by violin 2 (m. 23), and thrice in stretto (m. 27). Sequences of its most rapid rhythmic motive—three eighths plus two sixteenths—heighten the affect when played simultaneously by violins 1 and 2 (mm. 8–10 and 36) or by violin 1 and violone (mm. 13–15, 24–25, and 34–35).

The sober no. 2 features strettos of an eight-note subject, which is nothing other than a cadential formula.[129] It is heard thrice in measures 1–3, then eight times in measures 5–13. Sequentially descending scales with suspensions in measures 15–17 lead to a quasi-recapitulation, consisting of four entries in measures 18–23. A similar descent in measures 24–27 leads to the closing two entries in measures 28–29.

Four leaps begin the fierce, C-minor Vivace of no. 4.[130] Violin 1 ends the first exposition in measure 10 with a seven-note version of the fourteen-note subject. The opening half note is often replaced by three repeated eighths in the second and third expositions (mm. 10–20 and 24–35). This impelling repetition is not always placed at the head of the subject (see mm. 3, 5–6, and the quasi-episode in mm. 20–24), yet it is perceived as the head by the mid-point of the movement.[131]

The third movements, which are marked adagio, grave, or largo, are analogous to recitatives, in that they are brief (seven to twenty-five measures), through-composed, declamatory rather than lyrical, and in common time (except for no. 5, which is in $\frac{3}{2}$). They are in the tonic of a minor-key sonata and the relative minor of a major-key sonata.[132] Chordal texture is heard throughout no. 3 and at the beginnings of nos. 1, 5, and 6.[133] The other common texture consists of intertwining violins that create sorrowful suspensions over a melodic bass line; it is heard throughout nos. 2 and 4 (the grave C minor sonata) and in the second sections of nos. 1 and 5. The final cadence in nos. 1, 4, and 6 is followed by three chords: v^6–iv^6–V. Haym thus prepares the listener for the final movement, which should presumably be attacked *subito*.

The allegro or vivace finale is typically an ebullient conclusion in a meter—$\frac{3}{8}$, $\frac{6}{8}$, $\frac{12}{8}$, or $\frac{6}{4}$—that has not been utilized before. Only two are through-composed canzonas, with expositions and intervening episodes, rather than dance-like pieces in binary form. The $\frac{6}{4}$ Allegro in no. 4 retains the gravity heard throughout this C-minor sonata. Its violin 1 part is shown on plate 2. The nine-note subject features a quarter-note flow and is presented five times in three-part strettos (mm. 1, 12, 19, 29, and 36). Two episodes maintain the quarter-note flow (mm. 15 and 34), while the other three feature pairs of slurred eighth notes (mm. 6, 23, 41, and its echo in m. 46). The $\frac{6}{8}$ Vivace in no. 5 maintains the "academic" coherence and enlivens the rhythmic exuberance of this G-major sonata. Its sixteen-note subject is presented three times in three-part strettos (mm. 1, 13, and 25). Its lively rhythmic motive (an eighth, two sixteenths, and an eighth) is also featured in the intervening episodes (mm. 8 and 19). The coda (mm. 33–40) features a motive from the episodes, which is intensified by a chromatic rise in the continuo.

The four finales in binary form likewise serve to reinforce the prevailing affect of the sonata. Movements 2 and 4 of no. 1 in D minor are structurally symmetrical rather than daringly irregular. The finale is a $\frac{12}{8}$ jig, in which each half consists of two four-bar phrases plus an echo of the second. No. 2 in F major remains sober in its $\frac{3}{8}$ finale, because section one begins with stretto-like imitation, while section two begins with its quasi-inversion and continues by recapitulating the opening in measures 25–32. No. 3 in A minor maintains rhythmic drive in its $\frac{3}{8}$ Vivace finale. Each half begins chordally with a surprising three-bar unit, then continues with two- and four-bar units. Syncopations in measures 22–29 and swirls of sixteenth notes from measure 30 to the end intensify the rhythmic drive. The return to the tonic in measure 42 is followed by a quasi-recapitulation of the final phrase of the first half (cf. mm. 43–49 with 8–15). No. 6 in C major is the only finale in common time, and it resembles a sprightly allemande. Its second section develops earlier textures and motives (cf. mm. 1–5 with 11–15), then returns via sequences to the tonic, and culminates with a jubilant four and one-half measure phrase that is echoed.

The "Airs," or *Sonate da camera*, in Op. 1, Nos. 7–12

In this section, each chamber sonata will be discussed as a whole in order to focus upon its affect. Each opens with a slow preludio. Nos. 7–8 and 10 continue with a corrente in $\frac{3}{4}$ and end with a gavotta in $\frac{2}{2}$. Nos. 9 and 11–12 continue with an allemanda in $\frac{4}{4}$ and end with a giga in $\frac{12}{8}$.[134] In no. 7, a sarabanda separates the last two movements. In the other five sonatas, the third movement is not in binary form. Only no. 12 has an additional movement, a presto that precedes the closing giga. Only the middle two, nos. 9–10, are in minor keys.

The Preludio for no. 7 in B-flat major is a conventional prelude in that its time signature is $\frac{4}{4}$ and its tempo marking is Adagio. Its seventeen bars are based on the flowing motive of an eighth and two sixteenths, which the violins play in parallel thirds, then imitate and develop. The lively Corrente is based on the same motive. A dancing couple is implied by the violone's imitation of violin 1 at the beginning (mm. 1–7) and at the recapitulation (mm. 25–31). The ensuing Sarabanda is a conventional third movement in that its tempo marking is Adagio and its key is the relative minor. A grievous, bell-like tolling is conveyed by falling octaves in its bass and falling triads played in imitation by violins 1 and 2. The sorrowful affect climaxes in the final four bars, where the highest pitches are reached. The closing Gavotta, marked Presto, transforms the tolling octaves of the Sarabanda into ebullient ones, which are sometimes filled in with a scalar descent. A "couple" of violins "take turns" as they play the descent imitatively, then "join hands" by rendering and echoing it in parallel thirds (mm. 17–18 and 20–21).

The Preludio for no. 8 in D major maintains a steady eighth-note flow, which is ornamented by many pairs of slurred sixteenths in the violin parts. The Corrente, marked Vivace, maintains a steady quarter-note drive, upon which the violins superimpose a distinctive motive (two pairs of slurred eighths plus a quarter note). They usually play it successively, as if to represent a couple engaged in a rather wild rivalry. The somber Adagio in $\frac{3}{2}$ features intertwining parts as it modulates from the relative minor to the major tonic. In the Gavotta, the violins dance "arm-in-arm," that is, in parallel thirds or sixths, until they briefly "bow to one another" in the closing phrase (mm. 22–24, echoed in 26–28).

The Preludio for no. 10 in E minor resembles that for no. 8, because it is also in binary form and maintains a steady eighth-note flow, which is embellished by many pairs of slurred sixteenths in the violin parts. It recapitulates its opening bar in measures 14–15. The Corrente is a solo dance for violin 1, which repeats its opening motive at the beginning of the second half and at the recapitulation (m. 24). Violin 2 doubles violin 1 in measures 4–7, engages in imitative interplay with the violone at the end of each section (mm. 8–12 and 27–36), and both doubles and imitates violin 1 during the build-up to the recapitulation (mm. 18–23). The ensuing Grave in G major features intertwining violins, a walking bass, and suspensions on strong beats. A surprising forte ending follows the echo of the second phrase. The Gavotta resembles that of no. 8, in that the violins once again dance "arm-in-arm."

The $\frac{3}{2}$ Preludio for no. 9 in G minor is the only one in triple meter. It is by far the longest, because its first two Grave declamations are each followed by Allegro outbursts. The latter are based on a rising triadic motive that reaches its climactic pitch in measure 56, just before the second Allegro returns to the tonic key. The Allemanda, marked Andante, exhibits the most complex texture found in the three examples of this processional, ensemble dance in Haym's op. 1. The basic motive—two sixteenths plus eighths or longer note values—is "announced" by violin 1 as each half begins. All three instruments then participate in the motivic interplay heard in virtually all of the ensuing measures. The first two measures of interplay are recapitulated, then echoed, as the movement draws to a close (cf. mm. 2–3, 14–16, and 17–19). The ensuing Grave moves chromatically into G minor in measures 2–4, after which the parts intertwine until the half cadence in measure 8. The untroubled Giga features parallel thirds and sixths, with rhyming cadences at the ends of sections (cf. mm. 5–6 with 20–21).

The Preludio for no. 11 in A major features violin 1, which plays a three and one-half measure motive, repeats it a fifth higher, then recapitulates it on the original pitch level (mm. 1, 6, and 13). The movement cadences seven times on V or I, then ends with a three-chord transition to V. Violin 1 likewise dominates the first half of the Allemanda. As it plays five groups of sixteenths, violin 2 "fills the gaps" heard before groups 2–4 by playing four repeated sixteenths, then joins groups 4–5 by playing a parallel third below violin 1. After violin 1 plays its first group of sixteenths in the second half, violin 2 once again "fills in" with repeated sixteenths, but this time the first violin "reacts." In the developmental measures 10–15, it sequences (= mocks?) the repeated-note motive, imitates (= attacks?) three further "intrusions" by violin 2, joins the final playing of it in violin 2, then rises in "triumphant" arpeggios, as if it has won "the battle." The ensuing Adagio is the only third movement that remains in the tonic of a major key sonata. As in nos. 8–9, it begins chordally, and then gives way to intertwining parts. Its opening pair of intertwined measures is recapitulated (cf. mm. 6–7 and 13–14). In the closing Giga, violin 1 happily accepts and builds upon the descending fifth introduced by violin 2 (mm. 1, 3, 8, 15, 17, 21, 24, and 27). Violin 1 uses it to begin the exposition and recapitulation (mm. 1 and 16), to begin the closing statement within each half (mm. 5 and 22, echoed in 25), and to end the sequenced unit that begins the development (mm. 12–13).

The Preludio for no. 12 in G major begins lyrically, and then gives way to suspensions over a walking bass. The rhythmic motive of the Allemanda, marked Allegro e Puntato,[135] resembles that of the first movement of Beethoven's Fifth Symphony. It is doubled, usually in thirds or sixths, in measures 2–4, 13–14, and 15–17. In measures 2–4, violin 1 plays it six times, while the other two parts imitate one another and thus play it three times. In the last two climactic passages, the violone (originally played by Haym) plays it seven times, while the violins imitate one another. The Adagio in $\frac{3}{2}$ consists of a single phrase in the relative minor, followed by a three-chord transition to its dominant. It leads to the only extra movement in op. 1, a stormy *moto perpetuo,* marked Presto, which consists of constant sixteenth notes in violin 1, eighths in violin 2, and quarters in the violone. The closing Giga sounds playful, especially when the violins echo one another (mm. 3–11 and 26–36).

The "Free Sonatas" in *VI Sonate da camera,* Nos. 1–4

Estienne Roger published this undated score of six chamber sonatas at Amsterdam. He did not name a composer for the sixth sonata, list an accompanying instrument for the figured bass part, or provide a dance title for any movement. Because all six works are in minor keys and most of their fast movements are far from dance-like, they must be classified as "free" rather than "chamber" sonatas. Nos. 1–4 are headed "De Mr Haim," who is identified as "Nicola Francesco Haim Romano" on the title page. No. 5 is headed "Del Sig. M. Bitti," who is also named "M. Bitti" on the title page. Roger's advertisement in the *Amsterdamsche Courant* for 8 May 1710 provides his first name: "Sonate a flauto traverso, haubois o violino solo van Mrs. Haim e Martinetto Bitti, 2 gl."[136] Martino Bitti was a Genoese violinist employed by the Medici court at Florence from 1685 until his death in 1743.[137] In January and April 1704, Walsh attributed newly published "free" sonatas in A major to "Martino Betti" and "Martino Beity." At least the first one had been "perform'd by Sig^r^ Gasperini at the Theater Royall" in Drury Lane.[138] In December 1711, Walsh published eight of Martino Bitti's *sonate da camera,* first with an Italian, then with an English title page.[139] Martino never came to England, but on 6 April 1715 his brother Alessandro—"newly arriv'd from Italy"—played at one of Haym's concerts.[140] On 23 December 1718, "a new Concerto by the great Master Martino Betti" was performed at Stationer's Hall "by his Brother Alex. Betti."[141] Alexander served the Duke of Chandos in 1718–21[142] and was on the orchestral roster for the newly formed Royal Academy of Music in 1720.[143]

Nos. 1 and 3 by Haym, no. 5 by Bitti and no. 6 by an anonymous composer are in the somber key of C minor.[144] No. 1 begins Largo with a descending dotted-note motive that conveys a sorrowful affect (see plate 4). It is greatly strengthened after the midpoint, when an embellished version of it is played in parallel tenths (mm. 6–7, echoed in 8–9). The ensuing ¢ Vivace has a binary form and a tempestuous character. Each half begins with downward leaps of a fifth in eighth notes, continues with scalar sixteenths in parallel tenths, climaxes with thirty-seconds that descend a diminished fifth in the bass, and culminates with an arpeggiated leap in the violin that is "answered" by a vehement octave in the bass. The 3/4 Adagio is in the sepulchral key of F minor. Its somber mood is intensified by means of imitation, syncopation, and an echo of its closing sequence of suspensions. A 6/8 Allegro in binary form provides a lively, jig-like close. Its initial imitation also begins its second half and its recapitulation (m. 27). The bass part keeps the motion going throughout the suspension-filled passage that leads to the recapitulation, then takes the lead in the closing phrase, which is echoed.

In no. 3, the four movements are all in C minor and are all through-composed. They are fast-paced (three in ¢ and a finale in 6/8), and they feature a treble melody that is neither syncopated nor dissonant with the bass. The opening Adagio consists of three lyrical phrases (mm. 1, 8, and 14). The sixteenth-note flow of the ensuing Allegro is subtly based on a four-note motive. It is first heard by itself on beat 4 of measure 6, is imitated only on beats 2–4 of measure 19, but is interwoven into the flow from beat 3 of measure 1 onwards. The agitated, recitative-like Adagio is characterized by dotted quarter notes, large leaps in measures 3 and 5, and a tense ending that plunges into F minor and avoids an authentic cadence. The bass part opens the closing Allegro with six statements of a terse, militaristic, four-note rhythmic motive. The treble enters with two phrases that repeat, and then embellish, this terse motive. It continues with a metric displacement of it (mm. 10–11 and 17–18), and the movement maintains a severely belligerent character to the end.

In the remaining two sonatas, both fast movements are in binary form. Those of no. 2 in D minor resemble a 3/4 corrente and a 6/8 giga (which are not paired in Haym's op. 1). All four movements of no. 2 feature much motivic interplay between the two voices. In the opening Adagio, the development and recapitulation of measures 1–2 begin on beat 3 of measures 4 and 7, respectively. In the ensuing Allegro, a rhythmic motive is sequenced merrily during the first eight measures of the first half and the first four of the second. The hemiola cadence that completes the first half becomes the preoccupation of the second, which contains seven such cadences in measures 16–37. The final four are on D, and the final two are hocketed versions of the preceding two. The lyrically flowing 3/2 Adagio remains in D minor. The gigue-like Allegro that closes the work features a four-measure phrase that opens each half of the binary form, then is recapitulated and echoed at the end of the second half (mm. 20 and 26).

The fast movements of no. 4 in A minor are not dance-like. In the opening Largo, solemn suspensions over a walking bass force the melody to descend to a cadence in the tonic (mm. 3–7). Then, at its mid-point, it soars into the dominant key with a motive that includes pairs of slurred sixteenth notes, which are incorporated into the closing motive. The first half of the Allegro surprisingly halts for an authentic cadence on beats three and four of the opening measure. It also halts on the final two beats of measures 2–5, then abruptly cadences on the tonic, echoes it, and proceeds to a forte half-cadence. The second half begins with the same two-measure motive, adds a two-measure cadence, and then soars into the dominant with a sixteenth-note motive similar to the one heard in the opening Largo. It then returns to the halting motive (mm. 27–30 and 39–40), the soaring motive (mm. 31–33), the cadence from the first half (mm. 33–38), and an expanded, hocketed version of this cadence (mm. 41–49). Although the 3/4 Largo begins peaceably in C major, it is chromatically jolted into D minor before it resolves smoothly into A minor. It includes hemiola cadences in each key (mm. 8–10, 12–14, and 22–24, echoed in 27–29), then a surprising forte close. The final 3/4 Allegro is based on arpeggiated motives that rise energetically. One motive opens each half and returns twice: at a recapitulation in the dominant key (mm. 28–29) and in the final two forte bars. Another motive rises sequentially to a climax in each half (mm. 7–10 and 41–44, echoed in 48–51).

Notes on Performance

In this volume, many of the editor's thoughts concerning the proper affect, speed, articulation, ornamentation, and location of the structural climax of a movement are given in the foregoing analyses and in the "Editorial Methods" portion of the critical report. This section will comment first on the meanings of "foreign words" found in Haym's works, then on the instrumentation of the two collections contained in this volume.

Haym's op. 1 was published in 1703, the same year that Sébastien de Brossard's *Dictionaire de musique* was published by Christophe Ballard in Paris. Brossard's folio volume, which expanded his 1701 *Dictionaire des termes grecs, latins et italiens,*[145] defined many Italian terms. His definitions were the main source for *A Short Explication of Such Foreign Words, as are made use of in Musick Books,* which was printed for and conceivably compiled by J[ohn] Brotherton in 1724. It contains about 420 entries on ninety-six pages; about 88 percent are Italian words, 10 percent are French, and 2 percent are Greek or Latin.[146] *A Short Explication* provides definitions for almost all of the foreign words found in this edition. Its definitions have been reprinted together with those from many other sources in Graham Strahle, *An Early Music Dictionary: Musical Terms from British Sources, 1500–1740* (1995), which is an indispensable reference tool, since it reveals the meaning of performance indications before and during Haym's active years in England.

In terms of relative speeds, we learn from *A Short Explication* that adagio is "the slowest Movement in Musick," and that grave is "somewhat faster than ADAGIO, and slower than LARGO." Vivace means "with Life and Spirit," and is "a Degree of Movement between LARGO and ALLEGRO, but more inclining to the latter than the former." Allegro "must be performed in a gay, brisk, lively, and pleasant Manner, yet without Hurry or Precipitation." Finally, presto means "Fast or Quick." In 1728, Ephraim Chambers called these markings "the six Distinctions of Time," but listed grave rather than adagio as the slowest, and noted "that the Movements of the same Name, as *Adagio* or *Allegro,* are swifter in Triple than in Common Time."[147] In Haym's opp. 1–2, ninety-two movements are headed as follows: 33 adagio, 24 allegro, 12 vivace, 9 grave, 5 largo, 5 andante, and 4 presto.[148] Note that andante is not one of the "Distinctions of Time." It called instead for a steady beat and crisp articulation, and it heads three contrapuntal canzonas and two solemn allemandes in Haym's opp. 1–2.[149]

In Haym's opp. 1–2, six titles are found: allemanda occurs nine times; gavotta, giga, and preludio six times each; corrente three times, and sarabanda once. The last three titles are found only in op. 1. According to *A Short Explication,* preludio is "much the same as OVERTURE." Four of Haym's are marked C adagio, one is C largo, and one is 3/2 with three grave and two allegro sections. Each of the other titles identifies a specific "air" that was also a dance. The allemanda and gavotta utilize common time and binary form, but the latter is far simpler than the former, because it consists entirely of four-bar units "of a brisk, lively Nature." In Haym's opp. 1–2, the gavotta always serves as a swift finale. One is marked C presto; two are ¢ allegro; one is ¢ vivace; and two are ¢ without any tempo marking. The character of the allemanda was not "explicated" in 1724, but Chambers defined it in 1728 as "grave, solemn Musick, where the Measure is good, and the Movement slow."[150] In Haym's chamber sonatas, the solemn allemanda is always placed second, which is the focal movement in all his sonatas—it being the "home" of the contrapuntal canzona in his "free" sonatas. Five allemandes are marked allegro, two are andante, one is allegro e puntato, and one is largo e puntato. By means of the last three markings, Haym specifically requested a steady beat and a detached style of playing.

The giga and sarabanda are "always in Triple Time." The latter is "commonly play'd very Grave and Serious," while the former ranged from "slow" to "brisk and lively." Haym employed the title sarabanda only for op. 1, no. 7.iii, which is a 3/2 adagio. Ten other third movements in opp. 1–2 are marked 3/2 adagio or 3/2 grave, but they are not in binary form. Each 12/8 or 6/8 giga in Haym's opp. 1–2 is "brisk and lively": it serves as the vivace, allegro, or presto finale.[151] His only other dance air, the corrente, was not defined by the "explicator," but Chambers in 1728 termed the courant, currant, or curranto a piece in which the "Air . . . is ordinarily noted in Triples of Minims; the Parts to be repeated twice. . . . The *courant* is the most common of all the Dances practis'd in *England.*"[152] Haym marks it 3/4 allegro and places it at the focal point, that is, second in the sonata, an honor the canzona, allemanda, and corrente share.

All the sonatas in Haym's op. 1 are like the chamber sonatas in Corelli's opp. 2 and 4, in that they are scored for two violins and a bowed or plucked bass instrument. The bowed instrument named on Haym's title page and in the bass partbook is the violone. The plucked instrument named on the title page is the cembalo, but in the bass partbook it is the leuto.[153] According to extant program booklets for *accademie* presented in Rome by students at the Seminario Romano, Giovanni Antonio Haym was an instructor "per l'arcileuto e violoncello" in 1695, 1697, and 1699, while Nicola Francesco Haym was an instructor "per il violone" in 1697 and "per l'arcileuto e violoncello" in 1699.[154] When the violoncello played a continuo part, it was frequently called the violone in Italy.[155] This is because the bizarre term violoncello—which literally means a viol that is large (*-one*) and small (*-ello*)—was apparently coined at Bologna in 1665 and did not begin to spread elsewhere until the 1680s and '90s.[156] In Haym's op. 2, the bass part is—as in op. 1—labeled "violone o leuto." Only when the bowed bass instrument supplants violin 2 in op. 2, nos. 10–11, is its florid part—which is written in the violin 2 partbook—labeled "violoncello." Since Haym played the violone/violoncello, it seems reasonable to assume that this instrument should play the bass line together with a plucked instrument, namely, a cembalo/harpsichord[157] or a lute, archlute, or theorbo.[158] In Roger's advertisements for op. 1, the instrumentation is listed as "due violini e basso o arcileuto."[159]

The title of the collection *VI Sonate da camera a flauto traversa, haubois, o violino solo* lists three treble instruments but no bass instrument. Since the transverse flute and oboe were popular in northern Europe and the violin was gaining popularity there, Roger presumably hoped to triple his sales by naming all three instruments on the title page. Indeed, his advertisements of works intended "pour violon, flute et hautbois" extend from 1696 until at least 1712.[160] He advertised the Haym/Bitti collection in 1710 as "Sonate a flauto traverso, haubois o violino solo," in 1712 as "Six sonates à un hautbois & Basse continue," and in 1716 as "Sei sonate a violino o haubois solo e bc."[161] Why he omitted flute or flute and violin from the last two advertisements is unknown. Between 1728 and 1736, John Walsh likewise titled at least four of his publications *Solos for a German Flute, a Hoboy or Violin*.[162] Walsh specified that the "thorough bass" was "for the harpsichord or bass violin," i.e., violoncello. The passages of thirty-second notes in the bass part of Haym's no. 1.ii clearly illustrate that a cellist is required, because such repeated notes are not idiomatic for the harpsichord.

Notes

1. GB-Ckc, Ms. 206, p. 134: "Io nacqui l'anno 1678 alli 6 di luglio a undeci hore e un quarto di mattina secondo l'uso d'Italia. In Roma." Haym wrote this comment in an English score, which is the only source for his two Roman oratorios, *David sponsæ restitutus* (1699) and *I dui luminari del Tebro* (1700). See Lowell Lindgren, "The Accomplishments of the Learned and Ingenious Nicola Francesco Haym (1678–1729)," *Studi Musicali* 16 (1987): 332–33. Note that 6 July in the "Italian [=New] Style" is equivalent to 26 June in the Old Style, which was retained in England until 1752. Note also that GB-Ckc, Ms. 206, is in the same hand as GB-Cfm, Mus. Ms. 44 (olim 24.F.4), which is dated "Fine 4 Novemb. 1704" (fol. 186v), and includes (ff. 118v–120) Haym's first known aria text, "La cagion de' miei tormenti," set to music by Giacomo Greber.

2. At least eight Haims who held city offices and one who became a monk during this period are listed in Richard Lipp, ed., "Die Füssener Chronik des Färbermeisters Hans Faigele (1618–1640): Eine heimatkundliche Quelle im Tiroler Landesmuseum Ferdinandeum," *Alt Füssen* (1990): 195, 203, 206–7, and 209; (1991): 209; (1992): 135–36; (1994): 242; (1995): 154–55; (1996): 123 and 129; (1997): 153–57; and (1998): 153–54 and 156–57. Sebastiano's father might have been Christoph Haim, the town clerk from 21 September 1633 until his death from the plague on 17 October 1634; see ibid. (1995): 155 and (1996): 129. His widow became a midwife on 6 February 1637 and then left Füssen on 30 November 1639; see ibid. (1997): 154 and (1998): 154.

3. See *The New Grove Dictionary of Music and Musicians*, 2d ed. (hereafter *NG2*), s.v. "Füssen," by Adolf Layer and Erich Tremmel; and Adolf Layer, *Die Allgäuer Lauten- und Geigenmacher: ein Kapitel schwäbischer Kulturleistung für Europa* (Augsburg: Verlag der Schwäbischen Forschungsgemeinschaft, 1978).

4. Friedrich Noack, *Das Deutschtum in Rom seit dem Ausgang des Mittelalters* (Stuttgart: Deutsche Verlags-Anstalt, 1927), 1:237 and 2:233. The information given in Noack has been reiterated in Richard Bletschacher, *Die Lauten- und Geigenmacher des Füssener Landes* (Hofheim am Taunus: Friedrich Hofmeister, 1978), 196; Layer, *Die Allgäuer Lauten- und Geigenmacher,* 99, 141, and 160; Patrizio Barbieri, "Cembalaro, organaro, chitarraro e fabbricatore di corde armoniche nella *Polyanthea technica* di Pinaroli (1718–32), con notizie sui liutai e cembalari operanti a Roma," *Recercare: Rivista per lo studio e la pratica della musica antica* 1 (1989): 192–93; and René Vannes, *Dictionnaire universel des luthiers,* 3d ed. (Spa, Belgium: Les Amis de la Musique, 1999), 1:146 and 2:169. Bletschacher and especially Layer summarize the careers of a few other instrument makers named Haim.

5. Lindgren, "The Accomplishments," 248–51.

6. According to his obituary in *The Weekly Medley* for 9 August 1729 (hereafter "Obituary").

7. Barbara Turpini was conjecturally the mother of Giovanni Antonio. He was probably about fifteen years older than Nicola Francesco, whose mother was named Elena (Lindgren, "The Accomplishments," 248–50). Fifteen scholarly studies that document or discuss Roman performances by Giovanni Antonio, Nicola Francesco, Pietro Antonio, and/or Pietro's son Sebastiano Haym (1713–88) are cited in Lindgren, "The Accomplishments," 248–50 n. 7, 10, 13, and 14. Additional details are provided in Hans Joachim Marx, "Die 'Giustificazioni della Casa Pamphilj' als musikgeschichtliche Quelle," *Studi Musicali* 12 (1983): 148–49, 152, 158, 163, and 170 (see nos. 26, 34, 47, 65, 85, and 129); Jean Lionnet, *La Musique a Saint-Louis des Français de Rome au XVII° siècle (deuxième partie),* Note d'Archivio per la storia musicale; supplemento, new series, vol. 4 (Venice: Fondazione Levi, 1986), 146–48, 150, 152, 165, 167, 169, 171–73, 175, 178–79, 181, 185, 187–88, 190, 192–93, 195, 197, 199, and 203; Giancarlo Rostirolla, "Domenico Scarlatti e la Congregazione dei Musici di Santa Cecilia," in *Händel e gli Scarlatti a Roma,* ed. Nino Pirrotta and Agostino Ziino (Florence: Leo S. Olschki, 1987), 220, 238, and 248; Rostirolla, "La professione di strumentista a Roma nel Sei e Settecento," *Studi Musicali* 23 (1994): 90, 107–8, 113–14, 118–19, 122, 154, and 158; and Stefano La Via, "Il cardinale Ottoboni e la musica: nuovi documenti (1700–1740), nuove letture e ipotesi," in *Intorno a Locatelli: Studi in occasione del tricentenario della nascita di Pietro Antonio Locatelli (1695–1764),* ed. Albert Dunning (Lucca: Libreria Musicale Italiana, 1995), 1:387, 390, 392, 394–97, 399–400, 402, 404, 411–18, 420–21, 423–25, 427–42, 445–46, 482–84, 492–93, and 502.

8. The movements by Quirino are also printed in part 2 of this edition.

9. He is presumably the cellist named "Nicola" on a list of Roman musicians drawn up for Gio. Paolo Colonna between mid-August and mid-September 1694. It is printed in Oscar Mischiati, "Una statistica della musica a Roma nel 1694," *Note d'Archivio per la Storia Musicale,* new series 1 (1983): 222. On the same list, "Gio. Antonio Aimme" is named among both the ten contrabassists and the eight lutenists (ibid., 223). NB: Haym was variously spelled: Aim, Aimme, Haiam, Haim, Haime, Hayem, Haÿm, Hayme, Heim, Heyam, Higham, Hyam, etc.

10. Lowell Lindgren, "Il dramma musicale a Roma durante la carriera di Alessandro Scarlatti (1669–1725)," in *Le muse galanti: La musica a Roma nel Settecento,* ed. Bruno Cagli (Rome: Istituto della Enciclopedia Italiana, 1985), 55–57.

11. Nos. 72, 84, 128, 137–38, 145, 148, and 151 in Hans Joachim Marx, "Die Musik am Hofe Pietro Kardinal Ottobonis unter Arcangelo Corelli," *Analecta Musicologica* 5 (1968): 143, 147, 153–56, and 171.

12. Ibid., 143 (nos. 69bis/g–h and 72) and 162–77 (index). The number of players was "rounded" upwards to 100 and 150 in two *avvisi* (handwritten news reports), cited in Lindgren, "Il dramma musicale a Roma," 56.

13. Alberto Cametti, "La Società del Centesimo presso la Congregazione di Santa Cecilia (1688)," in *Annuario della Regia Accademia di Santa Cecilia, 1920–21* (Rome: Manuzio, 1921), 6, and Remo Giazotto, *Quattro secoli di storia dell'Accademia Nazionale di Santa Cecilia* (Verona: Mondadori, 1970), 1:264, 268, 275–76, 280, and 367. Giazotto includes facsimiles of documents that list Haym as one of the twenty-two players and thirty-three singers at a Second Vespers for Santa Cecilia, as one of the twenty who played at the Chapel of Sant'Agnese on 13 September 1695, and as an ill "brother" who received the usual gift of six *giuli* on 20 September 1699.

14. *Le aquile romane* (1695), fol. 7v, *Pallade togata e armata* (1697), fol. 4v, and *Li giuochi d'Apollo all'urna del secolo* (1699), fol. 4v. They were printed in Rome by Gio. Giacomo Komarek and are extant at I-Rn, 34.5.F.6/1, I-Rn, 34.8.B.6/12, and GB-Lbl, 838.m.22/168, respectively. See "Notes on Performance" below for comments concerning the identity of the violone and the violoncello.

15. See note 1 above.

16. On 2 August 1700, William Sherard, who served Wriothesley Russell, wrote to Cosimi: "Quant'al virtuoso suo compagno, sua Eccellenza lascia a lui di condurlo seco, o no, come crederà più a proposito." Sherard's letter is kept with the "carte varie del musico Niccolò Cosimi" in I-Rf. Much of his letter is printed in Lowell Lindgren, "Nicola Cosimi in London, 1701–1705," *Studi Musicali* 11 (1982): 232–33.

17. Lindgren, "Nicola Cosimi," 229–30 and 233.

18. Gladys Scott Thomson, *The Russells in Bloomsbury, 1669–1771* (London: Jonathan Cape, 1940), 86–92 and 121–30.

19. On 24 December 1711, Haym received a quarterly payment of £12 10s from the duchess dowager. His receipt terms it a "full" payment for the five quarters of salary (£62 10s) owed to him on 4 June 1711 and a "full" recompense "of all other demands" (Lindgren, "The Accomplishments," 253). He thus resigned his right to claim payment for four more quarters of service. Receipts are currently housed at Woburn Abbey, the Duke of Bedford's seat.

20. According to Haym's theatrical petition of 12 January 1708, printed in *Vice Chamberlain Coke's Theatrical Papers, 1706–1715,* ed. Judith Milhous and Robert D. Hume (Carbondale: Southern Illinois University Press, 1982), 57.

21. "Obituary."

22. Cosimi's financial diary lists about thirty performances in 1701–3 for patrons other than Bedford. In 1704–5, he received three large payments from Baltimore; each of them represented a five-month series of private concerts, which he presumably led. See Lindgren, "Nicola Cosimi," 234–35.

23. "L'Onore che goderono appena nate queste mie composizioni del benignissimo gradimento, con cui l'E[ccellenza] V[ostra] si degnò qualificarle nel tempo della sua dimora in Roma, le rende si ardite ora, che con le stampe conpariscono a gl'occhi del Mondo." The process of engraving and printing at least 124 copies of his sonatas took one year, from 1 November 1701 to 9 November 1702. Roger of Amsterdam published a second edition in 1704. See Lindgren, "Nicola Cosimi," 239–42, and François Lesure, *Bibliographie des éditions musicales publiées par Estienne Roger et Michel-Charles Le Cène (Amsterdam, 1696–1743)* (Paris: Société Française de Musicologie, 1969), 42. Only one other work by Cosimi is known to be extant: a "Sinfonia" for solo violin and continuo, which survives in a Roman copy at GB-Lcm, Ms. 1199.

24. *A General History of Music,* ed. Frank Mercer (London: Foulis, 1935), 2:444. A brief analysis of them is given in Lindgren, "Nicola Cosimi," 242–43.

25. Lindgren, "Nicola Cosimi," 239.

26. In letters written to Cosimi on 20 August and 15 October [1702], Visconti, who was in London, lamented the absence of his friends Cosimi and Haym, who were in the country; see Lindgren, "Nicola Cosimi," 237–38. When he played at a concert on 6 November 1702, a newspaper advertisement listed him as "Signior Gasparino, the famous Musician that plays upon the Violin, newly come from Rome." This citation is given in Michael Tilmouth, "A Calendar of References to Music in Newspapers Published in London and the Provinces (1660–1719)," *R. M. A. Research Chronicle* 1 (1961): 45.

27. The contents of eleven other collections, dated 1682–99, are listed in Claudio Sartori, *Bibliografia della musica strumentale italiana stampata in Italia fino al 1700* (Florence: Leo S. Olschki, 1952), 496–97, 500–1, 514–15, 520–22, 549–50, 560–61, 580–81, 585, 592–93, and 610. Ten of them are listed in the midst of an instructive article by Angela Lepore, "La Sonata a tre in ambito corelliano," *Intorno a Locatelli,* 1:552–54, 557–60, 562–65, and 567–69. During the 1680s and 1690s, Bologna and Venice were the main centers for the publication of trio sonatas. Lepore, "La Sonata a tre in ambito corelliano," 1:587–99, provides a list of 247 Italians who composed trio sonatas in the seventeenth and eighteenth centuries. See also Lepore, "Le 'primitie dell'ingegno': Sonate a tre a Roma al tempo di Corelli," in *Studi corelliani 5: Atti del quinto congresso internazionale, Fusignano, 9–11 September 1994,* ed. Stefano La Via, Quaderni della Rivista italiana di musicologia, vol. 33 (Florence: L. S. Olschki, 1996), 329–45.

28. James Sherard wrote: "I am encourag'd to hope **your Grace** will vouchsafe the same reception you was [*sic*] pleas'd to give them when you did me the Honour to hear them perform'd." His op. 1 was first advertised on 16 September 1701, according to Michael Tilmouth, "James Sherard: An English Amateur Composer," *Music & Letters* 47 (1966): 317.

29. Roger did not publish Sherard's op. 2 until 1715 or 1716, that is, until after the duke had died in 1711. A facsimile edition (Oxford and New York: Oxford University Press, 1986) adds a realization of the basso continuo by Ian Clarke and an introduction by Margaret Gilmore. A scribal copy with Sherard's autograph corrections is in GB-Ob, Ms. Mus. Sch. D.252; see *NG2,* s.v. "Sherard, James," by Michael Tilmouth and Robert Thompson.

30. Haym's title page is reproduced as plate 1. Theirs are in Tilmouth, "James Sherard: An English Amateur Composer," facing p. 299, and Lindgren, "Nicola Cosimi," facing p. 237, respectively.

31. John Hawkins, *A General History of the Science and Practice of Music* (London, 1853; reprint, New York: Dover, 1963), 675. It is presumably identical with the portrait now owned by the Faculty of Music at Oxford University. It became the model for subsequent English engravings. See Hans Joachim Marx, "Probleme der Corelli-Ikonographie," *Nuovi studi corelliani: Atti del secondo congresso internazionale, Fusignano, 5–8 September 1974,* ed. Giulia Giachin, Quaderni della Rivista italiana di

musicologia, vol. 4 (Florence: Olschki, 1978), 15–21, and Peter Allsop, *Arcangelo Corelli: New Orpheus of Our Times* (Oxford: Oxford University Press, 1999), 58.

32. The complete dedications for Haym's opp. 1 and 2 appear in this edition, as well as in Lindgren, "The Accomplishments," 335 and 337.

33. Lesure, *Bibliographie des éditions musicales,* 43 and 68, and the appended facsimile of *Catalogue de livres de musique, imprimés a Amsterdam, chez Michel Charles Le Cène* (Amsterdam, [1735]), 32 and 51. The date 1737 is handwritten on the title page of this copy of Le Cène's *Catalogue,* because it—according to information kindly provided by Rudolf Rasch—left his shop in 1737, when the five most recent titles were handwritten on the final page. Dr. Rasch also kindly informed me that Emanuel-Jean de la Coste, who purchased the deceased Le Cène's stock in 1743 (as noted in Lesure, *Bibliographie des éditions musicales,* 29–30), retained the old price for Haym's opp. 1–2 in his *Catalogue des livres de musique, imprimés à Amsterdam, chez Estienne Roger et Michel Charles Le Cène* [1743].

34. Two receipts are printed in Thomson, *The Russells in Bloomsbury,* 132. One lists the amounts paid to five singers (Mrs. Campion, Mrs. Lindsey, The Boy, Mr. Hughes, and Mr. Bourdon) "for performing in Mr. Weldon's Prize Music in Lincoln's Inn Fields for His Grace The Duke of Bedford." The premiere of Weldon's setting had been given at Drury Lane on 6 May 1701; see *The London Stage, 1660–1800, Part 2: 1700–29,* ed. Emmett L. Avery (Carbondale: Southern Illinois University Press, 1960), 11. For a modern edition, see John Weldon, *The Judgment of Paris,* ed. David W. Music, Recent Researches in the Music of the Baroque Era, vol. 94 (Madison: A-R Editions, 1999).

35. See 18 January at Drury Lane and 1 February at Lincoln's Inn Fields in *The London Stage, 1660–1800, Part 2,* 54–55.

36. *The Whole Volume Compleat Intituled The Monthly Masks of Vocal Musick, Containing All the Choisest Songs by the Best Masters made for the Play-houses, Publick Consorts and Other Occasions for the Year 1704* (London, 1704). Walsh's dedication has been reprinted in William C. Smith, *A Bibliography of the Musical Works Published by John Walsh during the Years 1695–1720* (London: The Bibliographical Society, 1948; reprint, 1968), 52.

37. Letter written by William Sherard on 2 August 1700, printed in Lindgren, "Nicola Cosimi," 233: "Sua Eccellenza la prega di procurarla 20 o 30 Cantate di megliori, alcune a voce sola, gl'altri con violini &c."

38. Thomson, *The Russells in Bloomsbury,* 130. The guest instrumentalists received far less: the lutenist Francesco Lodi received five guineas, while a transverse flute player from Bologna received three. The alto Pietragrua was in England early in 1702; see Lindgren, "Nicola Cosimi," 237, and *NG2,* s.v. "Pietragrua, Carlo Luigi," by Roland Wurtz and Paul Corneilson. The singer "Walentino" might have been Ranuccio Valentini or Valentino Urbani. Both were eunuchs, and no performance in 1702 is listed for either in Claudio Sartori, *I libretti italiani a stampa dalle origini al 1800* (Cuneo, 1990–94), Indici, 2:655–56, s.v. "Urbani, Valentino," and 659, s.v. "Valentino, Ranuccio."

39. See Lindgren, "The Accomplishments," 336–37. His autograph manuscript was sold by Sotheby, Wilkinson, and Hodge on 3 June 1903. Its present whereabouts is unknown.

40. "Obituary." For information concerning other cantatas known to have been composed by Haym, see Lindgren, "The Accomplishments," 333–34, 336–37, 339, and 343. Two additional cantatas have subsequently been found in English sources: *Aprimi il petto Amore* (1712), for alto and continuo, in B-Bc, Ms. XY.25769, pp. 43–50, and *E qual invido velo,* for soprano, two flutes and continuo, in US-Idt (Truman Presidential Library), [Giovanni Bononcini], *Songs in the New Opera, call'd Camilla, as they are perform'd at the Theatre Royall* (London, 1706), Ms. appendix, pp. 205–15.

41. Lindgren, "Nicola Cosimi," 236.

42. Ibid., 236–37, and *The London Stage, 1660–1800, Part 2,* new version, comp. and ed. Judith Milhous and Robert D. Hume, forthcoming. Their source is a list signed by John Eccles in GB-Lbl, Add. Ms. 61420, fol. 13. I am very grateful to them for supplying me with a draft of their new version.

43. *The Post-Man* for 25 and 27 September and 2 October 1705, reprinted in Smith, *A Bibliography of . . . the Years 1695–1720,* 57–58.

44. "Obituary."

45. *The Post-Man* for 18 October 1705, reprinted in Smith, *A Bibliography of . . . the Years 1695–1720,* 58. For Roger's Amsterdam advertisement of 1706 (which does not mention Haym), see Lesure, *Bibliographie des éditions musicales,* 46. The rivalry between Roger and Walsh extended from 1698 to 1746; see Rudolf Rasch, "Estienne Roger and John Walsh: Patterns of Competition between Early-18th-Century Dutch and English Music Publishing," in *The North Sea and Culture (1550–1800),* ed. Juliette Roding and Lex Heerma van Voss (Hilversum: Verloren, 1996), 396–407.

46. They are in D-B, GB-CDp, and a private collection.

47. Roger's reprint of 1702 is incorrectly dated 1700 and Haym's edition is conjecturally dated 1708 in *Répertoire International des Sources Musicales* (*RISM*), series A/1: *Einzeldrucke vor 1800* (Kassel: Bärenreiter, 1971–), C 3806 and C 3807. Roger dedicated his reprint to Jacob Klein (the Elder), dancing master at the Amsterdam Theater. Haym's edition has a newly engraved title page and has no dedicatee. I am very grateful to Dr. Rasch for supplying me with his observations concerning Roger's reprint of 1702 and Haym's edition of 1706.

48. Advertisement in *The Daily Courant* for her appearance at the Queen's Theatre on 17 November 1705, cited in *The London Stage, 1660–1800, Part 2,* 107.

49. Lindgren, "The Accomplishments," 258–59.

50. The "Articles of Agreement" are reproduced in facsimile in the appendix to Giovanni Bononcini, *Camilla: Royal College of Music, Ms. 779,* ed. Lowell Lindgren, Music for London Entertainment: 1660–1800, E/1 (London: Stainer & Bell, 1990).

51. Advertisement in *The Daily Courant,* partly cited in *The London Stage, 1660–1800, Part 2,* 115–16. Giuseppe Fedeli, called Saggione, mainly played the double bass; see Lowell Lindgren, "Italian Violoncellists and Some Violoncello Solos Published in Eighteenth-Century Britain," in *Music in Eighteenth-Century Britain,* ed. David Wyn Jones (Aldershot, Hants, UK, and Burlington, Vt: Ashgate, 2000), 148.

52. *The Daily Courant* for 16 and 23 February, cited in *The London Stage, 1660–1800, Part 2,* 117–18.

53. *The Daily Courant* for 3 April 1706, summarily cited in *The London Stage, 1660–1800, Part 2,* 122.

54. *Vice-Chamberlain Coke's Theatrical Papers,* 56–57.

55. Several versions of this painting survive. See the reproductions in Lindgren, "The Accomplishments," plate 1; Christopher Hogwood, *Handel* (London: Thames and Hudson, 1984), color plate IV; Annalisa Scarpa Sonino, *Marco Ricci* (Milan: Berenice, 1991), plates 61–62; and *NG2,* s.v. "L'Epine, Margherita de," by Winton Dean. Dean incorrectly identifies Haym as the harpsichordist.

56. Two slightly different versions of this painting survive. Both are discussed and reproduced in Scarpa Sonino, *Marco Ricci,* 118, 126, 150, and plates 63 and 65. Plate 65 in Scarpa Sonino is identical to plate 2 in Lindgren, "The Accomplishments," and plate 1 in this volume. Plate 63 in Scarpa Sonino, which is also reproduced in Judith Milhous and Curtis Price, "Harpsichords in the London Theatres, 1697–1715," *Early Music* 18 (1990): 38, differs in details; e.g., the harpsichordist looks at the score rather than at Haym. For a further discussion of the paintings, see Lindgren, "The Accomplishments," 268–69.

57. I am very grateful to Peter Allsop, who made this observation in July 2000, then strengthened it greatly in August 2000, when he sent me a color copy of the watercolor of Mount Edgcumbe by "W. de Busc," which is now in the Plymouth City Museum and Art Gallery. The portraits that hang to the left and right of the landscape have previously and tentatively been respectively identified as the painters Marco and his

uncle Sebastiano Ricci, both of whom worked in England between 1708 and 1716. Dr. Allsop has suggested that the right-hand portrait of an individual who seems to be holding a dog may instead depict Richard Edgcumbe. Allsop finds that it resembles the possible portrait of Edgcumbe printed in a Mount Edgcumbe guidebook and adds that a dog was known to be Edgcumbe's constant companion.

58. *Vice-Chamberlain Coke's Theatrical Papers,* 159–60, reprinted in Graydon Beeks, " 'Exit, Pursued by a Bear': The Haymarket Opera Orchestra and Handel's Arrival in England," *Händel-Jahrbuch* 42/43 (1996/1997): 67.

59. See note 74 below.

60. See Lindgren, "The Accomplishments," 272–77.

61. Nos. 258 and 278, dated 26 December 1711 and 18 January 1712, reprinted in *The Spectator,* ed. Donald F. Bond (Oxford: Clarendon Press, 1965), 2:505–7 and 584–85. In no. 302, for 15 February 1712, Charles Lilly's advertisement (not reprinted by Bond) reported that "the Subscription is 2 Guineas for Eight Times" and is "almost full."

62. No. 31 for 16 April 1713, reprinted in *The Guardian,* ed. John Calhoun Stephens (Lexington: University Press of Kentucky, 1982), 134. The five concerts—on 17 and 24 April, and 1, 8, and 27 May 1713—are listed in *The London Stage, 1660–1800, Part 2,* 300–303. The concert of 24 April featured "several Entertainments of Singing by the Baroness and another Scholar of Signor Haym, who never appeared in Publick" (see Lindgren, "The Accomplishments," 276). The latter was presumably "Mrs. Paulina," who is named in the advertisement for 27 May.

63. At this time, they were raising two (adopted?) boys, "Jack d'Haym" and "Mr. Davis." The couple apparently moved to Wardour Street before the death of the "Baronessa d'Haym," who was buried at St. Anne's, Soho, on 20 December 1724. Davis was an actor at the French Theatre in the Haymarket in spring 1735, by which time he had "more than once endeavour'd to divert the Town in a Poetical as well as Musical way." See Lindgren, "The Accomplishments," 256–61, 266, 268–71, 276–77, and 282–84.

64. *The London Stage, 1660–1800, Part 2,* 318, 350, 394, and 446. Alessandro was the brother of Martino Bitti, the composer of the fifth sonata in *VI Sonate da camera a flauto traversa, haubois o violino solo* (Amsterdam, [1710]). The first four sonatas are by Haym and are printed at the end of this volume.

65. Margaret Crum, "An Oxford Music Club, 1690–1719," *Bodleian Library Record* 9 (1973–78): 94. This performance (presumably of op. 1, nos. 1–7) was given at one of the monthly "stewards' nights," at which no guest was allowed.

66. Graydon Beeks, "Handel and Music for the Earl of Carnarvon," in *Bach, Handel, Scarlatti: Tercentenary Essays,* ed. Peter Williams (Cambridge: Cambridge University Press, 1985), 3 and 8.

67. The autograph, GB-Lbl, Add. Ms. 62651, calls for two boy sopranos, a bass, two violinists, an oboist, a "traversa," a "violone" (played by Haym), and an organist. See Lindgren, "The Accomplishments," 278, 294–95, and 347–48, and Graydon Beeks, "The *Chandos Anthems* of Haym, Handel and Pepusch," *Göttinger Händel-Beitrage* 5 (1993): 161–93.

68. He certainly adapted *Etearco* (1711), *Dorinda* (1712), *Creso* (1714), and *Lucio Vero* (1715), and he perhaps redid *Almahide* (1710), *Ernelinda* (1713), *Arminio* (1714), and *Vincislao* (1717). The 313 librettos named in his sale catalog of 9–18 March 1730 include the sources for most of his adaptations. These librettos are listed in alphabetical order in Elizabeth Gibson, *The Royal Academy of Music, 1719–1728: The Institution and Its Directors* (New York and London: Garland, 1989), 439–65.

69. Judith Milhous and Robert D. Hume, "New Light on Handel and the Royal Academy of Music in 1720," *Theatre Journal* 35 (1983): 159–61.

70. "Obituary."

71. Rolli termed his own London librettos "dramatici scheletri," but Haym's have significantly less recitative than Rolli's. They are thus more skeletal, i.e., further from Metastasian amplitude. See Lindgren, "The Accomplishments," 307.

72. Haym's adaptations are discussed in Lindgren, "The Accomplishments," 260–61, 289–314, 338–46, and 348–63. When Haym died in 1729, he was helping Handel and Heidegger plan a new musical academy. Thus, he is possibly responsible for at least some of the alterations in three texts—*Partenope, Ormisda,* and *Venceslao*—that were produced in 1730–31. If we count these three, the number of operas that Haym might have adapted for London productions is thirty-five; nineteen are certainly by him.

73. "Obituary."

74. Charles Gildon, *The Life of Mr. Thomas Betterton* (London, 1710; reprint, London: Frank Cass, 1970), 166–67, identified "Seignior *H[aym]* or some Creature of his" as the author of the "Notes." Gildon also gave Haym credit for the appended satire, entitled "A Critical Discourse on Opera's and Musick in England," because "this Author puts a great Stress on the *Taking* of his Compositions, and the Miscarriage of those of others." This attribution must be wrong, because the writer of the hilarious "Discourse" is surely a native-born Englishman with a keen sense of satirical wit.

75. *The Daily Courant* for 28 April 1716. Interested individuals were invited to obtain a free copy of the printed "proposals" and view a ten-folio "abstract" of the engravings; a copy of both items is extant in GB-Lbl, 1602/437. The medals were owned by eighteen British collectors and by Oxford University. Volume 1 includes a list of eighty-eight subscribers for 109 copies. In volume 2, fol. 6v, Haym noted that a list of additional subscribers would be printed at the beginning of volume 3 (which was projected, but never published). For a general description, see Lindgren, "The Accomplishments," 277–78 and 314–19.

76. It became his pet. See *Del tesoro britannico,* 2:124–25, the foldout plate signed "NH," and the translation, entitled *An Abridgment of the Second Volume of the British Treasury,* 2:36–37.

77. Lindgren, "The Accomplishments," 315.

78. Ibid., 320.

79. Ibid., 321–22. The plates, engraved by Gerard van der Gucht, were modeled on those of Bernardo Castello, published in the Genoa edition of 1590. Did Haym make corrections in any of the plates? According to Haym's obituary in *The Weekly Medley,* "the Knowledge he had in Medals is sufficiently known by his Work entitled Tesoro Britannico. He design'd very well, which was of great Service to him in correcting the Plates of his different Works." Such works could include any musical or non-musical work for which the plates were engraved in London.

80. Ibid., 322–24.

81. Ibid., 279–82. The name of the group was later changed to Academy of Ancient Musick.

82. *The Monthly Catalogue* 38 (June 1726): 70.

83. *The Flying-Post, or Weekly Medley* for 29 March and 12 April 1729. I am very grateful to Elizabeth Gibson, who kindly told me of these notices and provided me with her transcripts of them.

84. "Obituary."

85. Lindgren, "The Accomplishments," facing p. 299, reproduces the copy in the British Museum, Department of Prints and Drawings, s.v. "Engravings by G. Vandergucht (acq. 1927.10.8.351)."

86. In the original engraving—which I have not seen—another head would have been placed above Cuzzoni's, and the names of the designer and engraver would have been placed at the bottom left and right. Cuzzoni's "head" has been reproduced in *Die Musik in Geschichte und Gegenwart* (1949–68), 2:col. 1829; *Enciclopedia della Musica,* ed. Claudio Sartori, 4 vols. (Milan: Rizzoli, 1963–64), 1:plate 292, facing p. 583; and *Enciclopedia della Musica,* ed. Sartori, 6 vols. (Milan: Rizzoli, 1972), 2:223. No designer's or engraver's name is shown on these reproductions. On 18 October 1989, Ruth Blume kindly replied to my inquiry after examining the engraving in the MGG

archive. She reported that the difficult-to-read designer's name might be B[enjamin] Deimar, while the engraver's name is J[ames] Caldwall. It is, of course, possible that the difficult-to-read name is N. Haim rather than B. Deimar. The same portrait with a new background is attributed to "E. Seeman pinx." and "J. Caldwall sculp." in Hawkins, *A General History,* facing 872.

87. *The Flying-Post, or Weekly Medley* for 12 April 1729.

88. Hawkins, *A General History,* 821–22, reprints Haym's plan and proposals from this otherwise unknown "printed copy."

89. Thomson, *The Russells in Bloomsbury,* 138.

90. See, for example, Michael Jaffé, *The Devonshire Collection of Drawings* (London: Phaidon, 1994), vol. 2, *Roman and Neapolitan Schools,* 163, 218, 246–48, 253, and 269; vol. 3, *Bolognese and Emilian Schools,* 126; and vol. 4, *Venetian and North Italian Schools,* 207; and Margorie B. Cohn, *A Noble Collection: The Spencer Albums of Old Master Prints* (Cambridge: Harvard University Art Museums, Fogg Art Museum, 1992), 74–77 (where NH is identified as Nathaniel Hillier rather than Nicola Haym). See also two volumes in the series *Italian Drawings in the Department of Prints and Drawings in the British Museum* (London: Trustees of the British Museum): Philip Pouncey and J. A. Gere, *Raphael and His Circle* (1962), 169–70, and A. E. Popham, *Artists Working in Parma in the Sixteenth Century* (1967), 94.

91. *A Catalogue of the Entire Collection of the Learned and Ingenious* Antiquarian, *Mr.* Nicola Haym, *(Deceas'd) . . . Which will be* Sold *by* Auction . . . *at* Mr. *Cock's* Auction-Room. See Lindgren, "The Accomplishments," 327–28.

92. *A Catalogue of the Large and Valuable Library of Books, lately belonging to the Learned and Ingenious* Antiquarian, *Mr.* Nicola Haym, *(Deceas'd.) . . . To be Sold by* Auction *. . . at Mr. Cock's Auction-Room.* See Lindgren, "The Accomplishments," 328–29.

93. Lindgren, "Il dramma musicale a Roma," 39–40. Because of several wars, the only good years for English grand tours during the span 1688–1713 were 1697–1702; see Jeremy Black, "On the Grand Tour in 1699–1700," *The Seventeenth Century* 2 (1987): 199–213. Black, 203–9, cites passages that concern Richard Creed's five months in Loreto and Rome during the Holy Year of 1700, which was Haym's last year in the papal city.

94. "Obituary."

95. "I never met with any Man that suffer'd his Passions to hurry him away so much, whilst he was playing on the Violin, as the famous *Arcangelo Corelli;* whose Eyes will sometimes turn as red as Fire; his Countenance will be distorted, his Eye-Balls roll as in an Agony, and he gives in so much to what he is doing that he doth not look like the same Man" (*A Comparison,* 21 n).

96. See note 27 above.

97. *A Comparison,* 32 n. One anonymous and, unfortunately, far from trustworthy commentator who lived in late-eighteenth-century Rome declared that Haym "perfected his art in the light of instructions from Arcangelo Corelli." His comment is cited in Giazotto, *Quattro secoli . . . di Santa Cecilia,* 276: "Nicola Haim, suonatore di violoncello e autore di suonate, aveva perfezionato la sua arte al lume degli insegnamenti di Arcangelo Corelli, che in quegli anni teneva a Roma una rinomata scuola di violino, viola, violetta e violone o violoncello di che anch'egli si dilettava. L'Haim fu della Congregazione delli Sig.ri Musici di Roma ivi restando presente sino al giorno di sua morte che avvenne il 24 settembre 1704[!]."

98. Between 1708 and 1729, Haym was employed at the Queen's/King's Theatre in the Haymarket, where he worked only with operatic performances, which were not supplemented by independent, inter-act instrumental music.

99. Roger's booksellers in London included Francis Vaillant, Isaac Vaillant (1706–11), Henry Ribotteau (1711–19), and later members of the Vaillant family. Most of the instrumental music published by Roger through 1721 is listed in *An Account of Printed Musick for Violins, Hautboys, Flutes, and Other Instruments, by Several Masters,* which is a separately-paged attachment to *A Short Explication of Such Foreign Words as are made use of in Musick Books* (London: J[ohn] Brotherton, 1724). *An Account* includes Haym's op. 2 in three categories (pp. 7, 13, and 15) and the *VI Sonate da camera* in two (pp. 8 and 11). The entry on p. 15 should read "op. 1, 2," and the omission of op. 1 is presumably an oversight. All items listed in *An Account* could presumably be ordered at Brotherton's shop in 1724. In the copy of *An Account* in US-Wc, ML108.A2539, "Sould by John Walsh . . ." has been pasted over "by Several Masters" on the title page, and "*Apoll[o]'s Feast* . . . £1 1 0," which is a collection of arias published by Walsh in 1726, has been added in hand at the bottom of the first page of the catalogue. The last seven titles listed in *An Account,* p. 20, were published only by Walsh in London. It thus appears that Walsh was also selling Roger's publications, at least ca. 1726. The chamber ensemble listings (which exclude those for solo instrumentalists and orchestral groups) found in *An Account* are transcribed in Michael Tilmouth, "Chamber Music in England, 1675–1720" (Ph.D. diss., Christ's College, Cambridge, 1959), 1:393–98.

100. Anik Devriès, *Édition et commerce de la musique gravèe a Paris dans la première moitié du XVIIIe siècle: Les Boivin, Les LeClerc* (Geneva: Èditions Minkoff, 1976), 87 and 198. LeClerc's price for the volume was 6 livres tournois, which—according to Rudolf Rasch—was equivalent to about 3 Dutch guilders.

101. For opp. 1–2, see note 33 above. For *VI Sonate da camera,* see Lesure, *Bibliographie des éditions musicales,* 50 and 86; the appended facsimile of *Catalogue de . . . Michel Charles Le Cène,* 34 and 41; and the catalogue of La Coste.

102. Nos. 300, 833–34, 2803, and 2816 in *Catalogue of the Music Library, Instruments and Other Property of Nicolas Selhof, Sold in The Hague; 1759,* facsimile of the auction catalogue, introduced by A. Hyatt King (Amsterdam: Frits Knuf, 1973), 103, 134, and 240–41.

103. Rudolf Rasch kindly provided this information concerning the stock and valuation in 1743. It has been derived from Amsterdam, Gemeentearchief, Notarieel Archief, n. 10226, stuk nr. 539. Rasch discusses this source in "I manoscritti musicali nel lascito di Michel-Charles Le Cène (1743)," *Intorno a Locatelli,* 2:1039–70.

104. Roger North, *On Music, being a Selection from His Essays Written during the Years c.1695–1728,* ed. John Wilson (London: Novello, 1959), 310–11.

105. Hawkins, *A General History,* 678. The Corellian features in Sherard's sonatas are discussed in Tilmouth, "James Sherard: An English Amateur Composer," 320–22.

106. Burney, *A General History,* 2:444. Their stylistic features are discussed in Lindgren, "Nicola Cosimi," 242–43.

107. This evaluation was printed anonymously in Abraham Rees, *The Cyclopædia,* 2d ed. (London, 1802–20), vol. 17 (1811): s.v. "Haym," and reprinted in Alexander Chalmers, *The General Biographical Dictionary,* 2d ed. (London, 1812–17), 17:268. Chalmers cites "Ree's Cyclopædia, by Dr. Burney" as his source.

108. The solo sonatas printed in this volume have been available in a commercial facsimile edition since 1984; it is described in the critical report. The only commercial edition of a trio sonata has been David Lasocki's of op. 2, no. 6 (New York: Hargail Music Press, 1978).

109. Tilmouth, "Chamber Music in England, 1675–1720," 1:307–8. Tilmouth, 2:182–92, contains handwritten scorings of op. 1, no. 4, and the first two movements of op. 2, no. 10.

110. Lindgren, "The Accomplishments," 287–88. See ibid., 365–80, for editions of op. 1, nos. 4–5.

111. "La Sonata a tre in ambito corelliano," 560–62. Lepore's data for Haym's op. 1 need more than a dozen corrections. (NB: In references to sonata movements, a dot is preceded by an arabic sonata number and followed by a roman movement number.) The form of no. 6.iv is 10 + 22 measures (not 32 × 2) and that for no. 7.iv is 8 + 14 measures (not 22 × 2). The meter of no. 4.i is $\mathbf{C}^{3}_{2}$ in the violone partbook; that of no. 8.iii is $\mathbf{C}^{3}_{2}$ and that of no. 8.iv is $\frac{2}{2}$ in the violin 2 and violone partbooks. The lengths for five units must be shortened by one measure: no.

4.iv is 51 measures (not 52); no. 7.ii is 10 (not 11) + 27 measures; no. 9.ii is 8 (not 9) + 12 measures; no. 11.ii is 8 (not 9) + 13 measures; and no. 12.ii is 6 (not 7) + 12 measures. The key of no. 11.iii is *La* (not *Mi*), while the keys of three other third movements cannot be properly represented by Lepore's single key. She gives *re* for no. 2.iii, which intermingles *re* and *Fa*, then ends in *Fa*. She gives *la* for no. 3.iii, which consists of two measures in *re*, one measure in *sol*, then four measures in *La/la*. She gives *do* for no. 9.iii, which begins with a *do* chord, then has one measure in *fa* and six measures in *sol*.

112. Allsop, *Arcangelo Corelli*, 154. Allsop does not refer to the pernicious papal, political, and natural causes mentioned above, which were largely responsible for this "mass migration of musicians."

113. Ibid., 28 and 155.

114. Ibid., 155–57. Their publications are listed in Sartori, *Bibliografia della musica strumentale italiana*, 560–61, 585, and 610, and in Lepore, "La Sonata a tre in ambito corelliano," 552–53 and 568–69.

115. Allsop, *Arcangelo Corelli*, 157. As noted above, Hawkins, like Burney, customarily related sonatas written around 1700 to Corelli's; but his statement concerning Haym's opp. 1–2 does not do so: "He published two operas of Sonatas for two violins and a bass, which shew him to have been an able master" (Hawkins, *A General History*, 820).

116. Allsop, *Arcangelo Corelli*, 158. NB: Corelli's op. 6 was not printed until 1714, a decade after Haym's op. 2 was published.

117. For two rather different explications of modal writing, both of which are primarily based upon Giovanni Maria Bononcini's *Musico prattico*, op. 8 (Bologna, 1673), see Allsop, *Arcangelo Corelli*, 99–104, and Gregory Barnett, "Modal Theory, Church Keys, and the Sonata at the End of the Seventeenth Century," *Journal of the American Musicological Society* 51 (1998): 245–82. For a survey of German, French, and English treatises of the late 1600s and early 1700s, see Joel Lester, *Between Modes and Keys: German Theory, 1592–1802* (Stuyvesant, N. Y.: Pendragon, 1989), 77–132 and 163–234.

118. According to Allsop, *Arcangelo Corelli*, 102, table 6.5, they are modally in D minor. No. 1, with a final on D, is untransposed, while no. 4, with a final on C, is transposed down a tone. The transposed mode of op. 1, no. 1, is also employed for nos. 1 and 3 in *VI Sonate da camera*.

119. Thomas Morley, *A Plain and Easy Introduction to Practical Music (1597)*, ed. R. Alec Harman, 2d ed. (New York: W. W. Norton, 1963), 296. Morley is here describing the fantasy: "In this may more art be shown than in any other music because the composer is tied to nothing [e.g., a text or a dance-like structure], but that he may add, diminish, and alter at his pleasure." For some intriguing conjectures concerning the relationship of Renaissance canzonas to Baroque sonatas, see Ruth Halle Rowen, *Early Chamber Music* (New York: King's Crown Press, 1949), 21–38, and Eleanor Selfridge-Field, "Canzona and Sonata: Some Differences in Social Identity," *International Review of the Aesthetics and Sociology of Music* 9 (1978): 111–19.

120. North, *On Music . . . c.1695–1728*, 180, and *Roger North's "The Musicall Grammarian 1728,"* ed. Mary Chan and Jamie C. Kassler (Cambridge: Cambridge University Press, 1990), 180. In this passage, North criticizes Sherard's fugues: "for altho repetition is good, too much is fastidious." Then he praises Corelli's: "tho driven thro variety enough, yet the air of the key is preserved."

121. Within the partbook, "Violone" heads even-numbered pages, and "O Leuto" (rather than "O Cembalo") heads odd-numbered pages.

122. Sartori, *Bibliografia della musica strumentale italiana*, nos. 1685a and 1694a, and Allsop, *Arcangelo Corelli*, 107.

123. Sartori, *Bibliografia della musica strumentale italiana*, nos. 1681a and 1689b, and Allsop, *Arcangelo Corelli*, 75–77 and 91.

124. Allsop, *Arcangelo Corelli*, 73–75, and Allsop, "Sonata da Chiesa—A Case of Mistaken Identity?" *The Consort* 53 (1997): 4–14.

125. *A Short Explication*, 74–75 (cited in Graham Strahle, *An Early Music Dictionary: Musical Terms from British Sources, 1500–1740* [Cambridge: Cambridge University Press, 1995], 338–39). The four solo sonatas printed at the end of this volume first appeared in *VI Sonate da camera* (1710), but they are "free" works rather than "airs." For surveys of the *da chiesa* and *da camera* modifiers, see John Daverio, "In Search of the *sonata da camera* before Corelli," *Acta Musicologica* 57 (1985): 195–214, and Sandra Mangsen, "The 'sonata da camera' before Corelli: A Renewed Search," *Music & Letters* 76 (1995): 19–31.

126. The lengths of nos. 2–6 will be doubled if the repetition signs that end them are observed. In Corelli's op. 1, five through-composed second movements likewise end with a repetition sign. In his op. 3, Corelli reduced this number to one. See tables 5.4 and 6.1 in Allsop, *Arcangelo Corelli*, 77 and 91.

127. See the listings for Baldassini's opp. 1 and 2 (1691 and 1699), Furloni's *Sinfonie* (1693) and Mannelli's op. 2 (1682) in Lepore, "La Sonata a tre in ambito corelliano," 552–53, 559–60, and 564–65. Purcell introduced the term canzona near the end of his discussion of three-part counterpoint in John Playford, *An Introduction to the Skill of Music*, 12th ed., corrected and amended by Henry Purcell (London, 1694; facsimile edition, with a new introduction by Franklin B. Zimmerman, New York: Da Capo Press, 1972), 175: "Most of these different sorts of *Fugeing* are used in *Sonata's*, the chiefest Instrumental Musick now in request, where you will find *Double* and *Treble Fuges* also reverted and augmented in their *Canzona's*, with a great deal of Art mixed with good Air, which is the Perfection of a Master." The contrapuntal meaning was not retained in *A Short Explication*, 19 (cited in Strahle, *An Early Music Dictionary*, 51), where canzone is equated with allegro. Perhaps this is because counterpoint was "a Way or Method of composing Musick, . . . now very little used" (*A Short Explication*, 24; cited in Strahle, *An Early Music Dictionary*, 94).

128. The second movements of nos. 3 and 5 are marked andante, no. 2 is marked allegro, and the remaining three are marked vivace. Allsop, *Arcangelo Corelli*, 157 n, declares: "The designation *andante* in several obviously quick second movements is taken to be a concession to Haim's English patrons!" His implication, that andante meant "not quick" to Haym and his contemporaries, is incorrect. Roger North identified andante as a humor rather than a tempo, wrote about "the *andante* or fuge," and defined andante as "a walking about full of concerne" (*On Music . . . c.1695–1728*, 100, 123, 180 n, and 194–96). According to *A Short Explication*, 10 (cited in Strahle, *An Early Music Dictionary*, 13), andante signified that the bass part must keep the time "very just and exact, and each Note made very equal and distinct the one from the other." The term is thus suitable for a movement filled with contrapuntal intricacies, because a successful rendition of it requires rhythmic precision. See note 149 below.

129. Allsop, *Arcangelo Corelli*, 10 and 157, notes that Denis Arnold termed this formula "a bit of Old Roman Counterpoint, and might be by anybody."

130. According to Tilmouth, "Chamber Music in England," 1:307, this Vivace "is based on a well-worn eighteenth-century cliché (the 'And with his stripes' theme, which served Corelli, Handel, Bach, Haydn, and Mozart in turn) but is none the worse for that."

131. Allsop, *Arcangelo Corelli*, 157, convincingly relates Haym's leaps and repeated notes to those in Corelli's op. 3, no. 4.iv.

132. In Corelli's op. 1, five of the six sonatas in major keys have a third movement in the relative minor.

133. According to Allsop, *Arcangelo Corelli*, 157, some of Haym's "perfunctory slow sections still act as little more than links." Nos. 1 and 3, each of them seven measures long, are the shortest, but they will be far from "perfunctory" if rendered dramatically and with judicious embellishment.

134. These dance pairs are not the norm for the thirty *sonate da camera* in Corelli's opp. 2, 4, and 5. Only two (op. 4, nos. 3 and 9) pair a corrente with a gavotta, and only five (op. 2, nos.

4 and 11, op. 4, nos. 6 and 12, and op. 5, no. 8) pair an allemanda with a giga. Corelli's dance titles are listed on tables 7.1 and 8.2 in Allsop, *Arcangelo Corelli,* 107 and 126.

135. According to *A Short Explication* (1724), 57 and 59, *pointe* means "the same as STACCATO, or SPICCATO," and *punto* is "a Point, a Character in Musick very well known." This is the first of three definitions cited in Strahle, *An Early Music Dictionary,* 14 and 279. The second is Nathan Bailey, *An Universal Etymological English Dictionary,* 3d ed. (London, 1726), s.v. "pointe": "to separate or divide each Note one from another, in a very plain and distinct Manner. *Ital. Punto,* a point." The third is William Tans'ur, *A Compleat Melody: or, The Harmony of Sion,* 3d ed. (London, 1736), 67, who equates andante, picque, pointe, and spiccato.

136. I am grateful to Rudolf Rasch for kindly sending me his transcript of this advertisement. Note that the advertisement has "flauto traverso," which is correct, while the title page has "flauto traversa" [*sic*].

137. See *NG2,* s.v. "Bitti, Martino," by John Walter Hill; Mario Fabbri, "Due musicisti genovesi alla corte granducale medicea: Giovanni Maria Paglardi e Mar[t]ino Bitti," in *Musica piemontese e liguri,* ed. Adelmo Damerini and Gino Roncaglia, in Chigiana, vol. 16 (Florence: L. S. Olschki, 1959): 85 and 88; and Sartori, *I librettti italiani,* Indici, 1:355, s.v. "Bitti, Martino."

138. See nos. 413 [April 1704] and 414 [January 1704] in R. Alec Harman, *A Catalogue of the Printed Music and Books on Music in Durham Cathedral Library* (London: Oxford University Press, 1968), 67. See also nos. 143, 150, and 224 in Smith, *A Bibliography of . . . the Years 1695–1720,* 46, 48, and 71.

139. See no. 396, *Sonate a due, violino e basso, per suonarsi con flauto o'vero violino,* and no. 401, *Solo's for a flute, with a through bass for the harpsichord or bass violin,* in Smith, *A Bibliography of . . . the Years 1695–1720,* 119–21.

140. *The London Stage, 1660–1800, Part 2,* 350. For solos and concertos played by him in London between 1716 and 1722, see ibid., 403, 446, 452, 494, 521, and 676.

141. Tilmouth, "A Calendar of References to Music," 104. This concerto might have been printed in *Concerti a 6 e 7 instrumenti del signore Vivaldi, Torelli e Bitti* (Amsterdam, [ca. 1714]); see Lesure, *Bibliographie des éditions musicales,* 85, and the appended facsimile of *Catalogue de* Michel Charles Le Cène, 60. Walsh sold this print at London in 1718; see no. 550 in Smith, *A Bibliography of . . . the Years 1695–1720,* 157. According to Rudolf Rasch, Roger's collection contains six concertos; none is attributed to a composer, and none has thus far been identified with one of the Bitti brothers.

142. Beeks, "Handel and Music for the Earl of Carnarvon," 8 and 17.

143. Milhous and Hume, "New Light on Handel," 158–60. According to Philip A. Highfill, Jr., Kalman A. Burnim, and Edward A. Langhans, *A Biographical Dictionary of Actors, Actresses, Musicians, Dancers, Managers & Other Stage Personnel in London, 1660–1800* (Carbondale and Edwardsville: Southern Illinois University Press, 1973–93), 2:139, Alexander Bitti was paid for playing in Jamaica at some time between November 1727 and October 1730.

144. Bitti's sonata has three flats in its key signature. The others have only two.

145. *NG2,* s.v. "Brossard, Sébastien de," by Yolande de Brossard.

146. Strahle, *An Early Music Dictionary,* xx. Strahle declares that *A Short Explication* "is believed to have been written by John Christopher Pepusch," but this declaration represents too great a leap from the inconclusive suggestion made in Jamie C. Kassler, *The Science of Music in Britain, 1714–1830: A Catalogue of Writings, Lectures and Inventions* (New York and London: Garland, 1979), 2:1138. Indeed, Haym could have easily compiled *A Short Explication.* His own copy of Brossard's *Dictionaire de musique* is no. 618 in *A Catalogue of the Large and Valuable Library of Books, lately belonging to . . . Mr.* Nicola Haym, *(Deceas'd.),* 21.

147. Ephraim Chambers, *Cyclopædia: or, an Universal Dictionary of Arts and Sciences* (London, 1728), s.v. "Allegro" (cited in Strahle, *An Early Music Dictionary,* 10).

148. Seven of the second movements in opp. 1–2 have a second, slower tempo mark near their end. In six cases, it is adagio; in the seventh (op. 2, no. 2), it is largo. Adagio is similarly found near the end of the variation set in op. 2, no. 12, which has no tempo at the beginning. Two movements have no tempo mark at all; they are the gavottes in op. 2, nos. 7 and 8.

149. The canzonas are op. 1, nos. 3.ii in A minor and 5.ii in G major, and op. 2, no. 3.iv in G minor. The allemandes are op. 1, no. 9.ii in G minor and op. 2, no. 10.ii in A minor. See note 128 above.

150. Cited in Strahle, *An Early Music Dictionary,* 11.

151. Except in op. 2, no. 8, where it is followed by a gavotta.

152. Cited in Strahle, *An Early Music Dictionary,* 97 and 100. The corrente is the focus of the discussion in Peter Allsop, "*Da camera e da ballo—alla francese et all'italiana:* Functional and National Distinctions in Corelli's *sonate da camera,*" *Early Music* 26 (1998): 87–96.

153. Haym conjecturally played the bass part by himself, unless a trustworthy cembalist or archlutenist was present. As mentioned above (see the text for notes 121–23), two bass parts were typically printed for collections of church sonatas, and a second bass part was printed in 1705 by both Walsh and Roger for Corelli's chamber sonatas, opp. 2 and 4. If two bass parts had not been printed, two bass players could have read from the same score, as shown in Ricci's paintings of opera rehearsals (one of which is shown on plate 1). The publication of only one bass partbook does not therefore mean that only one instrumentalist could play the bass line, which is a main point made in two articles. They are by Niels Martin Jensen, "The Performance of Corelli's Chamber Music Reconsidered: Some Characteristics of Structure and Performance in Italian Instrumental Music in the Decades Preceding Corelli," in *Nuovissimi studi corelliani: Atti del terzo congresso internazionale, Fusignano, 4–7 September 1980,* ed. Sergio Durante and Pierluigi Petrobelli, Quaderni della Rivista italiana di musicologia, vol. 7 (Florence: L. S. Olschki, 1982), 241–49, and Sandra Mangsen, "The Trio Sonata in Pre-Corellian Prints: When Does 3 = 4?" *Performance Practice Review* 3 (1990): 138–64.

154. See note 14 above.

155. The term violone was also utilized for the "very large Bass Violin, or Double Bass," which was "used only in Great Consorts, as Operas, and other publick Musick" (*A Short Explication,* 90 [cited in Strahle, *An Early Music Dictionary,* 411]). In chamber music partbooks, violone meant violoncello during Haym's career. See David Watkin, "Corelli's Op. 5 Sonatas: 'Violino e violone o cimbalo'?" *Early Music* 24 (1996): 645–63; see also the late-eighteenth-century reference to "violone o violoncello" in note 97 above. The probable differences between the two during the 1600s are discussed in articles by Stephen Bonta, "From Violone to Violoncello: A Question of Strings?" and "Terminology for the Bass Violin in Seventeenth-Century Italy," *Journal of the American Musical Instrument Society* 3 (1977): 64–99 and 4 (1978): 5–42. When Haym arrived in London, the bass viol was the leading bass instrument, so the confusion was usually between viol and violoncello rather than violone and violoncello. See Lindgren, "Italian Violoncellists and Some Violoncello Solos," 125–29.

156. Stephen Bonta, "Corelli's Heritage: The Early Bass Violin in Italy," in *Studi corelliani 4: Atti del quarto congresso internazionale, Fusignano, 4–7 September 1986,* ed. Pierluigi Petrobelli and Gloria Staffieri, Quaderni della Rivista italiana di musicologia, vol. 22 (Florence: L. S. Olschki, 1990), 217–31.

157. Guidelines from five treatises of 1607–84 are given in Guido Morini, "Cenni sul basso continuo in Italia nel XVII secolo," *Studi corelliani* 4, 261–74. Guidelines derived from eight sources of ca. 1700–57 are given in Lars Ulrik Mortensen, " 'Unerringly tasteful?': Harpsichord Continuo in Corelli's Op. 5 Sonatas," *Early Music* 24 (1996): 665–79.

158. See Nigel North, *Continuo Playing on the Lute, Archlute, and Theorbo* (Bloomington and Indianapolis: Indiana University

Press, 1987); Lynda Sayce, "Continuo Lutes in 17th and 18th-Century England," *Early Music* 23 (1995): 667–84; Sylvia Garnsey, "The Use of Hand-Plucked Instruments in the Continuo Body: Nicola Matteis," *Music & Letters* 47 (1966): 135–40; Jessie Congleton, "The False Consonances of Musick: Nicola Matteis's 'Instructions for the Playing a True Base upon the Guitarre,' " *Early Music* 9 (1981): 463–69; and Marco Pesci, "Nuove propose di prassi esecutiva fondate su un inedito trattato di basso continuo per arciliuto," *Recercare: Rivista per lo studio e la pratica della musica antica* 8 (1996): 5–57.

159. See Lesure, *Bibliographie des èditions musicales,* 43 (1703) and 68 (1716).

160. The advertisements are cited ibid., 35–39, 42–46, 48, and 50.

161. See ibid., 50 and 86, for those of 1712 and 1716. The advertisement of 1710 has been cited above (see the text for note 136) and will be cited below (see the critical report, source B).

162. They contain works of Giovanni Battista Grano, Giovanni Boni, Francesco Barsanti, and Carlo Tessarini. See Richard A. McGowan, *Italian Baroque Solo Sonatas for the Recorder and the Flute* (Detroit: Information Coordinators, 1978), 20, 23, 27, and 45. McGowan does not list the Haym/Bitti collection of *VI Sonate da camera.*

Plate 1. Marco Ricci (?), Rehearsal of *Pyrrhus and Demetrius* in autumn 1708. The cellist, who seems to have stopped the rehearsal, is presumably Nicola Haym. Private collection, photo National Portrait Gallery. Reproduced by permission of the National Portrait Gallery, London.

DODECI SONATE, À TRÈ

Cioè due Violini, e Violone ò Cembalo, di

Nicola Francesco Haim Romano

Opera Prima

CONSECRATE

Al' Illus.^mo et Ecc.^mo Signore

IL SIG.^re WRIOTHESLY DUCA DI BEDFORD,

Marchese di Tavistok, Conte di Bedford, Barone Russell di Thornhaugh, Barone Howland di Streatham, Governatore, delle Provincie, di Bedford, Cambridg, e Middlesex, et Custos Rotulorum per la detta Provincia, et Cavaliero del' Nobbilis^mo Ordine della Giartiera

in Amsterdam per ESTIENNE ROGER 1703.

Plate 2. Title folio for each partbook of Nicola Francesco Haim, op. 1. Reproduced by permission of The Governing Body of Christ Church Library at Oxford University.

Plate 3. Nicola Francesco Haim, op. 1, end of Sonata No. 4 in C minor from the Violino primo partbook, p. 7. Note the duplication of E♭ in the key signature, the // indications for trills, and the engraver's flourish at the close. Reproduced by permission of The Governing Body of Christ Church Library at Oxford University.

Plate 4. Opening page of Sonata No. 1 in C minor "De Mr Haim" from *VI Sonate da Camera a Flauto Traversa, Haubois o Violino Solo* (Amsterdam, [1710]), 2. The title page attributes the work to "Nicola Francesco Haim Romano." Reproduced by permission of the Studio per Edizioni Scelte (S.P.E.S.), Florence, Italy.

Dodeci sonate a tre, Op. 1

Dedication

Consecrate | Al Illus.mo et Ecc.mo Signore | Il Sig.re Wriothesly Duca di Bedford, | Marchese di Tavistok, Conte di Bedford, Barone Russell di | Thornhaugh, Barone Howland di Streatham, Governatore, | delle Provincie, di Bedford, Cambridg, e Middlesex, | et Custos Rotulorum per la detta Provincia, | et Cavaliero del Nobbiliss.mo Ordine | della Giartiera

Eccellentissimo Prencipe

Se quanto sono più debboli gl'Edifici, hanno tanto più bisogno di sostentamento per frastornarli dalla caduta, qual'appoggio più saldo potevano trovare questi primi parti della mia penna, che l'esser fatti degni della protettione del'E. V., che oltre il merito inpareggiabile della Nascita, ha così fina intelligenza della Musica, che non havranno timore di non essere compatiti dal Pubblico, mentre non sono stati discari a gl'orecchi di V. E. nel udirli; Hora che gli li consacro, La supplico d'aggradire l'offerta benché picciola, stante che l'animo supplisce al mancamento delle mie Forze: Mi glorio intanto di potere adornare il fronte di queste mie compositioni, con il glorioso Nome del'E. V., et di sottoscrivermi qual sono

Londra li 15 Febraro 1703

Di V. E.

Umil.mo Devo.mo et Oblig.mo Servitore

Nicola Fran.co Haim

Dedicated to the Most Illustrious and Most Excellent Lord, Master Wriothesly, Duke of Bedford, Marquis of Tavistock, Count of Bedford, Baron Russell of Thornhaugh, Baron Howland of Streatham, Governor of the Counties of Bedford, Cambridge, and Middlesex, and Custos Rotulorum for the said Shire(s), and Knight of the Most Noble Order of the Garter

Most Excellent Prince

The weaker that structures are, the more need they have of support to prevent them from collapse. A very firm support will be found for these first fruits of my pen if they are considered worthy of the protection of Your Excellency, who, besides the peerless merit of your birth, has such a fine understanding of music that there will be no fear of nonacceptance by the public, provided that the works are not found unacceptable to the ears of Your Excellency while listening to them. Now that I dedicate them to you, I beg you to find the offering, although small, pleasing, since my intentions compensate for the lack of my abilities. It glories me meanwhile to be able to adorn the commencement of these, my compositions, with the glorious name of Your Excellency, and to write underneath that I am

London, 15 February 1703

Your Excellency's Most Humble, Most Devoted, and Most Obliged Servant

Nicola Fran.co Haim

Sonata No. 1 in D Minor
for Two Violins and Basso continuo

Adagio

Adagio e Piano
forte
forte
piano
forte
piano
forte
piano
Allegro
piano
piano
piano

piano
piano
piano

Sonata No. 2 in F Major
for Two Violins and Basso continuo

Adagio

Largo
[piano]
piano
[piano]
Allegro

piano
piano
piano
forte
forte
forte
[tr]
[tr]

Sonata No. 3 in A Minor
for Two Violins and Basso continuo

29
34
38
piano
piano
piano
Adagio
4

Vivace
8
16
24
32

39
4 ♯3
6
6
47
6
5
[tr]
4 ♯3
4 ♯3
4 ♯3
piano
piano
piano

Sonata No. 4 in C Minor
for Two Violins and Basso continuo

Vivace

Adagio

Adagio
Allegro

32
36
40
tr
44
piano
piano
piano
48

Sonata No. 5 in G Major
for Two Violins and Basso continuo

Andante

Grave
Vivace

piano
piano
piano

Sonata No. 6 in C Major
for Two Violins and Basso continuo

piano
piano
piano
forte
piano
forte
piano
forte
piano
Vivace

Adagio

Grave

forte
piano

Allegro

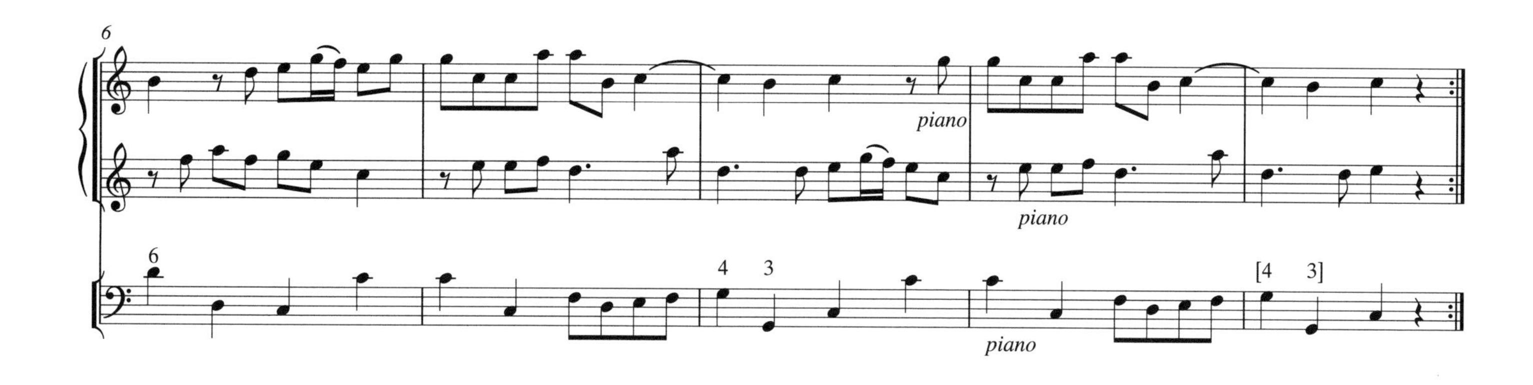
piano

piano
piano
piano

Sonata No. 7 in B-flat Major
for Two Violins and Basso continuo

Corrente. Allegro

piano
piano
piano
Sarabanda. Adagio

Gavotta. Presto
5
9
14
19
piano
piano
piano

Sonata No. 8 in D Major
for Two Violins and Basso continuo

Corrente. Vivace
6
11
17
23
[tr]
[6]

piano
piano
piano
Adagio

18
6
5
4 3
6
♯6
Gavotta. Allegro
7
5
♯
♯
♯
9
[6]
6
7
5
[4 3]
♯
14
[tr]
♯
6
♯
4
♯3
5
♯

18
[tr]
4
♯3
[tr]
4
3
22
6
4
[2]
[6]
26
piano
piano
6
4
[2]
piano
6
[tr]
4
3

Sonata No. 9 in G Minor
for Two Violins and Basso continuo

27
32
Grave
39
Allegro
44
48

53
6
♭
♮
57
6
♯
[tr]
4
♯3
62
piano
piano
6
♯4
2
6
4
♯3
67
6
♯4
2
6
4
♯3
piano
72
Grave
[𝄐]
[𝄐]
♭7
5
4
♯3

Allemanda. Andante

Grave
Giga. Vivace

piano
piano
piano

Sonata No. 10 in E Minor
for Two Violins and Basso continuo

Corrente. Allegro

28
piano
piano
piano
33
Grave
5
piano
piano
9
piano
forte
forte
forte

Gavotta. Vivace
[♯6]
6
♯
6 5
5
♯
6
[6]
6
[6]
♯
[6]
[tr]
4 ♯3
4 ♯3
4 3
piano
piano
4 ♯3
piano
4 ♯3

Sonata No. 11 in A Major
for Two Violins and Basso continuo

Allemanda. Allegro

16
[6]
piano
[tr]
piano
piano
19
Adagio
6
11

16
forte
piano
forte
piano
forte
piano
Giga. Allegro
4
7
10
1.
2.

13
6
♯4
6
6
6
5
4
♯3
16
6
5
6
19
6
6
4
♯3
22
6
6
[6
6]
4
3
piano
25
piano
6
6
[6
6]
4
3
piano

Sonata No. 12 in G Major
for Two Violins and Basso continuo

[tr]
piano
Adagio
forte
piano
Presto
[6]

Giga. Allegro
piano
[6]
4 3
4 ♯3
piano
piano
piano
♮5
♯6
6
[6]
♮7
5
4
♯3

From *VI Sonate da camera*

Sonata No. 1 in C Minor
for Transverse Flute, Oboe, or Violin Solo and Basso continuo

piano
Adagio

piano
piano
forte
forte
Allegro

piano
piano

Sonata No. 2 in D Minor
for Transverse Flute, Oboe, or Violin Solo and Basso continuo

11
17
22
28
33
piano
piano
Adagio

piano
piano
Allegro

17
22
piano
piano
27

Sonata No. 3 in C Minor
for Transverse Flute, Oboe, or Violin Solo and Basso continuo

f
piano
piano

Adagio
Allegro

piano
piano
forte
piano
forte
piano

Sonata No. 4 in A Minor
for Transverse Flute, Oboe, or Violin Solo and Basso continuo

piano
piano
forte
forte
piano
piano
forte
forte

piano
piano
forte
forte
piano
piano
Largo

piano
forte
Allegro

10
piano
piano
15
forte
forte
21
26
31
36

piano
piano
forte
forte

Critical Report

Sources

Source A

Dodeci sonate a trè, cioè due violini e violone o cembalo, di Nicola Francesco Haim romano, op. 1, was dedicated by Nicola Fran^{co} Haim to Wriothesly Russell, Duke of Bedford, on 15 February 1703, and was published in three partbooks "in Amsterdam per Estienne Roger, 1703." Each engraved image is 16.5 cm high by 20.2 cm long, and each trimmed page is usually 3 or 4 cm longer in each direction. Each partbook begins with the title page on fol. 1 (see plate 2) and dedication on fol. 2. Each continues with a blank page (p. 1), then with eight staves of music per page. Centered at the top of each music page is a word or two that identifies a part. Thus, "violino" appears on even-numbered, while "primo" or "secondo" appears on odd-numbered pages (see plate 3 for "primo," p. 7). Likewise, "violone" appears on even-numbered, while "o leuto" appears on odd-numbered pages. Their final pages are respectively headed "primo" (p. 23), "violino secondo" (p. 22), and "violone o leuto" (p. 22). The engraver ended every movement with a double barline, i.e., a pair of vertical lines that spans all five staff lines. At the end of every sonata (except violin 1, No. 2), he added a distinctive ornamental pattern. It ordinarily begins with a design that spans all five staff lines; then four to nine similar designs decrease gradually in size until they end with a single mark (usually a "c") on the middle line. Among the most elaborate designs are those that end violin 1, nos. 3, 4, and 6; violin 2, nos. 2, 5, 10, and 12; and violone, nos. 1–3, 8, and 10. Violin 1, no. 4, is shown on plate 3.

The five known exemplars are the following:

1. GB-Lbl, K.7.c.2/2. This copy consists only of proofs ("épreuves") for violin 1, pp. 1–23, and violin 2, pp. 1–22. At the end of the latter is a comment written in brown ink: "Do not be bothered by anything that is not cleanly or perfectly printed; since these are only proofs, pay attention only to mistakes, if there are any" (Ne prenez pas garde s'il y a quelque chose de malpropre & mal tiré; ce ne sont que des épreuves, ne vous attachez qu'aux fautes s'il y en a). The music is printed on only one side of each very thin page. The pages have been trimmed to 17.5 cm high by 21.2 cm wide. The edges of every page have been reinforced by pasted-on paper.

In each part, there is writing in brown ink on the blank page at the beginning (= p. 1). Placed at their center is "violino primo" or "violino secondo" followed by an ornamental design. At their upper right is "Correttione" followed by a list of missing fermatas. Their lists include four for violin 1 and one for violin 2. These five fermatas have been added within the proofs, as have three piano markings: one for violin 1 and two for violin 2. Each part also has one correction that is struck through. These ten "corrections" are in the hand of Nicola Haym, yet none of them appears in the printed copies listed below. Eight of them have been added to this edition in square brackets, and all are listed in the critical notes.

The eighteen items bound together in GB-Lbl, K.7.c.2 are trios. No bass part is present for Haym's op. 1 or for four other items. No. 1 in the volume is a manuscript copy of "Mr. Jenkins his 3 parts for 2 trebles and one bass." No. 2 is Haym's op. 1. Nos. 3–7 were printed in Amsterdam by Roger in 1696–97. Nos. 8–17 were printed in Amsterdam by Johan Philips Heus or Antoine Pointel before 1696, and eight of their prints (all except nos. 8 and 17) contain nothing but dance airs from Lully's operas. No. 18 is a later addition, which was printed at The Hague in 1778.

Haym might have once owned some or all of nos. 1–17, but the earliest known owner is identified by what appears to be a late-nineteenth-century bookplate, pasted onto the flyleaf that precedes each partbook. The shield on the bookplate includes the open hand of a baronet, three fleurs-de-lys and three roses. Above the shield is a dragon's head with wings, and below it are the dragon's feet, the motto "Æquo Adeste Animo," and the end of the dragon's tail. John Hopson, Archivist of The British Library, kindly examined this shield and identified it with the Cope baronetcy, which was created in 1611. The earliest baronet who could have owned nos. 1–17 is the fifth, Sir John Cope, who succeeded to the title in 1675 and died in 1721.[1]

"British Museum, 15 AP 1924" is stamped in red within an oval at the end of each part, while "Bound 1934" is stamped in blue within an oval inside the covers. According to Mr. Hopson, the red stamp identifies the date when the set of partbooks was purchased from Mrs. Blake, 12 Sherriff Road, West Hampstead. The invoice refers to it as "A collection of unique and rare chamber music (late 17th and 18th cent.). Including manuscript by John Jenkins and works by Veracini, C. Rosiers, H. Anders, B. Tonini, B. Bernardi, G. B. Vitali, G. B. Lulli etc. 3 vols. £15."

2. GB-Ob, Mus. Sch. E.509a–c. An older call number, which was written in pencil on each title page, has largely been erased: D.3.68 = 509a, D.3.69 = 509b, and D.3.70 = 509c.[2] Torn, frayed, and smudged pages mar the beginning of the violin 1 part and the endings of the other two partbooks. It is possible, though far from certain, that some smudges found within the parts were caused by performers turning pages with dirty fingers. In the GB-Ob and GB-Och copies, a sharp has been added in brown ink before no. 5.i, violin 1, measure 22, note 2.[3] The cardboard binding was presumably added in the twentieth century. A companion volume, GB-Ob, Mus. Sch. E.510a–c, contains Haym's op. 2.

3. GB-Och, Pr. Mus. 97–99. This set of partbooks probably formed part of the collection given by Henry Aldrich, Dean of Christ Church College and Cathedral from 1689 until his death in 1710, because it was in the Library at Christ Church by 1717.[4] Each partbook is bound in marbled paper over a flexible board, which may well date from the early 1700s. The pages have been neatly trimmed to a height of 18.2 cm and a width of 24.6 cm. Inside the front cover of each partbook is a bookplate with the shield of Christ Church above the words "Ædes Christi in Academia Oxoniensi." Above it is written in ink the current and former shelf mark: "97 = olim I.3.5," "98 = olim I.3.6," and "99 = olim I.3.7." A thin flyleaf is placed inside each cover. "G.2" is written in brown ink in the upper left corner of the opening flyleaf of each partbook. The condition of each part is pristine. No smudges are present, but the worn spine of each part and the sharp added in no. 5 (see GB-Ob above) may indicate that the parts were used.

4. US-Wc, M351.H56Op.1.Case. This call number includes both op. 1 and op. 2, and each bound partbook includes both prints. The bindings may well date from the eighteenth century. Each cover measures 20 cm high by 24.5 cm wide, and each end board is covered with worn brown suede. Each is embossed with black rectangular designs. The outer pair of rectangles is 18.5 cm high by 23.5 cm wide, and scallops run inside of them. The inner pair of rectangles is 7.5 cm high by 12 cm wide; a floral design runs between them, and scallops run outside of them. At each corner, three branches with leaves sprout diagonally outward, and the central one culminates with three flowers.[5] The spines and beginnings or endings of partbooks are rather frayed and darkened by dirt. A comparison of the copies in US-Wc and GB-Och revealed that they were identical, except for the accidental added in ink in GB-Och (and in GB-Ob).

5. NL-DHnoske. Rudolf Rasch informed me of this copy, which belonged to the Dutch violinist Willem Hendrik Noske (1918–95), brother to the musicologist Frits Noske (1920–93). His collection has recently been transferred from NL-DHgm to the Nederlands Muziek Instituut at The Hague, where it is inaccessible.[6]

Source B

VI Sonate da camera a flauto traversa, haubois o violino solo di Nicola Francesco Haim romano e M. Bitti was published in treble-bass score by Estienne Roger in Amsterdam. It includes "Sonata I [II, III, IV] de Mr Haim" on pages 2–15, "Sonata V del Sig. M. Bitti" on pages 15–18, and "Sonata VI" (without any attribution) on pages 19–21. Each page includes six pairs of staves, as shown on plate 4. Each movement ends with a double barline, i.e., with two vertical lines that span all five staff lines. At the end of each sonata, the engraver added about six vertical lines that gradually decrease in length, until a point on the middle line is reached. Haym's op. 2 of 1704 employs the same end-markings. The print was first advertised in the *Amsterdamsche Courant* for 8 May 1710: "Estienne Roger Boekverkoper, woonende tot Amsterdam op de Cingel bij Malta, verkoopt de . . . Sonate a flauto traverso, haubois o violino solo van Mrs. Haim e Martinetto Bitti, 2 gl."[7]

The only confirmed source is D-WD, Music Print No. 66, which is listed in Fritz Zobeley, *Die Musikalien der Grafen von Schönborn-Wiesentheid*, part 1, *Das Repertoire des Grafen Rudolf Franz Erwein von Schönborn (1677–1714)*, vol. 1, *Drucke aus den Jahren 1676 bis 1738* (Tutzing: Hans Schneider, 1967), 54–55. Zobeley lists the tempos and time signatures for each movement and gives the opening two measures of the treble part for each sonata. He also notes that a handwritten partbook for violoncello survives. The score and partbook both have plain, reddish-colored covers, which may well date from the early eighteenth century. Pasted on both front covers is a piece of white paper, which has a title written in brown ink.[8] The title on the paper pasted on the cover of the printed score is "Sonate a flauto traversiero, hauboy o violino solo del Nic. Franc. Haim romano et M. Bitti. lib. 2. sb 12." The title on the paper pasted on the cover of the partbook is "Violoncello. Sonate a flauto traversiero, Hauboy o violino solo del Nicol. Francesco Haÿm et M. Bitti. lib. 2." The partbook, which begins with a folio headed "Basso," is written on seven folios of eleven-stave paper with a foolscap watermark. It contains the tempo and dynamic markings found in the printed score, but omits the continuo figuration. It was undoubtedly copied for the lord of the manor, Count Rudolf Franz Erwein von Schönborn (1677–1754), who was a cellist.[9] The previous shelf mark, "SB 12," was presumably added on the score and part after 1900. The cello part also has an older number, "H4," which appears below "SB 12." There are no handwritten additions within the printed score.

A facsimile of *VI Sonate da camera* was published in 1984 by Studio Per Edizioni Scelte (S. P. E. S.) of Florence, Italy, as no. 1 in its series "Archivum Musicum: Flauto traversiere." In his introduction, Marcello Castellani discusses the composers, the works, and the likelihood that the treble part was intended primarily for a violin. He does not name the source for his facsimile edition. If it is the copy in D-WD, he has "cleansed" it—for example, by eliminating the stamp of the library, which should appear after "M. Bitti" on the title page. It will be good news, indeed, if a second copy survives, perhaps in private hands.

Editorial Methods

The current edition follows as closely as possible the 1703 set of parts for Haym's op. 1 and the 1710 score for

VI Sonate da camera. Titles for movements, tempo markings, clefs, key signatures, time signatures, slurs, ornaments, bass figures, dynamics, stem direction, and beaming have been altered minimally. Many cautionary accidentals have been eliminated, many tied notes have been replaced by their non-tied equivalents, and some brief rests in compound meters have been combined.

Tempo Markings

Tempo markings have been repositioned, in that they are always placed above the uppermost staff. Their original location was usually below the staff in each engraved part of 1703 and between the treble and bass staves in the score of 1710. In op. 1, nos. 7–12, tempos are usually combined with titles. In the original partbooks, each of these chamber sonatas begins with a tempo word *above* the staff and the word preludio below it. Such "vertical" placement for tempo and title words is employed for only two of the ensuing dance movements: no. 9.ii, an Andante/Allemanda, in each partbook, and no. 7.ii, an Allegro/Corrente, in only the violin 1 partbook. Title and tempo designations for the other dances (eleven in violin 1 and twelve in the other two partbooks) were originally placed together under the staff, e.g., Corrente Allegro for no. 7.ii in the violin 2 and violone partbooks. The present edition utilizes such "horizontal" placement for all nineteen titles found with tempo markings in op. 1, nos. 7–12, and it supplants the variable amount of space between the words with a period and a space, e.g., Gavotta. Presto for no. 7.iv.

Clefs and Signatures

The treble parts were originally written in the treble clef, while the continuo part was usually written in the bass clef. Wherever the tenor clef was utilized for the violone part in op. 1, it has been retained in this volume, as in no. 2.i, measures 4–6, and no. 2.iv, measures 5–7 and 29–31.

The unaltered key signatures utilized in this volume include four that do not correspond to modern tonality, because they lack one flat. They include one of the two sonatas in D minor (op. 1, no. 1) and all three that are in C minor (op. 1, no. 4, and *VI Sonate,* nos. 1 and 3; see plates 3 and 4). This edition does not include the duplicate accidentals found in the signatures for seven sonatas in the op. 1 partbooks. In these seven, the accidentals found near the top of the staff are given again near the bottom. Thus all five sonatas in sharp keys add f♯ on space 1, and one of them—in A major—also adds g♯ on line 2. The two sonatas that have as many as two flats in their signatures add e♭ on line 1, as shown on plate 3.

Ten time signatures are found in the engraved prints. Eight of them—C, ¢, $\frac{3}{2}$, $\frac{3}{4}$, $\frac{3}{8}$, $\frac{6}{4}$, $\frac{6}{8}$, and $\frac{12}{8}$—remain in use today, while two—¢$\frac{6}{8}$ and C$\frac{3}{2}$—were already disappearing from use in Haym's day. By then, the difference between C and ¢ was rather indistinct. According to Giovanni Maria Bononcini in 1673, "the moderns employ ¢ as if it were C, except they keep a somewhat faster beat" (da i moderni viene però usato come il primo, battendo solo alquanto più presto).[10] According to John Lenton in 1693, C and ¢ each indicated a "mood," and "the first of those Moods signifies a very solid or slow movement, the second quicker."[11] According to Henry Purcell in 1694, C is the "*slow* sort of *Common-Time,*" and ¢ "is a little faster."[12] According to Roger North in 1728, "the old marks of Comon Time quickening" began with C and ¢, but "now it is done by description, as adagio, grave, allegro, presto, prestissimo."[13]

In copies and editions of Giovanni Maria Bononcini's own collections, dances with triple time signatures are inconsistently prefixed with ¢ or C, and when the London edition of his op. 12 was published in October 1701, it eliminated both prefixes.[14] Lenton's only combination of C with 3 has the C placed under the 3, which is a "*Mood* . . . to three in a Barr" with "a very slow motion."[15] When Haym heads the closing movement of *VI Sonate,* no. 1, with the signature ¢$\frac{6}{8}$, he presumably calls for an exceptionally lively rendition of this gigue-like Allegro. By means of the signature C$\frac{3}{2}$, which heads his op. 1, nos. 4.i and 8.iii, Haym presumably calls for contemplative renditions of these slow movements. Yet even his op. 1 illustrates that the prefix was disappearing, because C precedes $\frac{3}{2}$ for nos. 4.i and 8.iii in the violone part, for only no. 8.iii in violin 2, and for neither movement in violin 1. The lower two parts also agree in their signature for no. 8.iv, which is ¢ rather than the C found in violin 1. The signatures found in the violone, which Haym played, have been adopted in this edition for all movements except no. 1.iv, in which the violone is written in C, while the other two parts are in $\frac{12}{8}$. The bass was presumably written in C because its shortest note value occupies one beat, i.e., a quarter note in C.[16]

Hemiola passages, which substitute three "imperfect" (i.e., undotted) values for two "perfect" (i.e., dotted) values, are somewhat obscured by the original notation. Hemiolas can be clarified by inserting a $\frac{3}{2}$ measure into a $\frac{3}{4}$ movement or a $\frac{3}{1}$ into a $\frac{3}{2}$ movement. In the engraved editions, this was done only for the three-chord transitions placed at the ends of *VI Sonate,* nos. 1.iii and 2.iii. The present edition has not added any such changes.[17] It has, however, clarified some hemiolas by eliminating ties between the third and fourth quarter notes in $\frac{6}{4}$ or the third and fourth eighth notes in $\frac{6}{8}$, so that the $\frac{3}{2}$ or $\frac{3}{4}$ meter is clear.[18]

Articulations and Ornaments

Each note should be bowed individually unless it occurs within a slur. In the engraved prints, slurs are quite common over pairs of notes, but they infrequently encompass groups of three, even in compound meter, or groups of four. Note, for example, that all slurs cover two rather than three notes in the jigs that end op. 1, nos. 11 and 12. Whenever a motivic pattern includes slurs for some but not all of its appearances, dashed slurs have been added to achieve a consistent articulation. Performers may choose to ignore any dashed slur, e.g., if they find it inadvisable or impractical for a violoncello to slur a passage precisely as a violin did. Apparent discrepancies between slurrings in the engraved prints have been retained. Two striking examples appear in jig-like finales. In op. 1, no. 1, the slurs in violin 1 cover the first two eighths in a beat, while those in violin 2 envelop all three. In *VI Sonate,* no. 1, three-note slurs appear at the opening, but two-note slurs replace them at the recapitulation (mm. 26–29).

Ornaments are left almost entirely to the discretion of performers. None are specified in *VI Sonate,* and an ornamental sign—which consists of two parallel, diagonal lines (//)[19]—is found in the violin parts for only three movements of op. 1. It is found fifteen times in no. 4.iv (see plate 3), but only once in no. 5.i and only once in no. 6.iv. In this edition, it has been replaced by *tr,* the abbreviation for trill. Performers in Haym's age were expected to vary some patterns during the repetition of each half of a dance[20] and to add the customary trills utilized in cadential formulas. Cadential trills have been added in square brackets only when one violin must play a trill in order to supply the 4–3 indicated in the bass figuration.[21] One "call" for embellishments may well be the fermatas found within and at the ends of slow movements.[22] Indeed, each fermata might have been placed precisely where an ornamental flourish was to be played.[23] Performers are advised to ignore most of the movement-ending fermatas and rests if they do not add a flourish.

Continuo Figures

The bass figures in the engraved prints are all represented in this edition. They are placed above the bass part in the sources. An accidental sign always precedes a number in this edition. In op. 1, an accidental is placed after a number whenever there is far less room for it before the number. Two other changes have been made. The first has been to replace some of the engraved sharps and flats with naturals. A natural has replaced any sharp that raises B♭ or E♭ by a half step, and a natural has replaced any flat that lowers F♯, C♯, or G♯ by a half-step. The second has been to replace three pitch-raising symbols found in *VI Sonate* with sharps or naturals. These symbols are the number 4 with a vertical slash through its lengthened "tail" and the numbers 5 and 6 with a diagonal slash through their extended "tops." These changes are not listed in the critical notes.

The figures in the engraved bass part of op. 1 are often crowded together. The figures 4♯3, for example, are typically engraved over three bass notes. The 4 belongs with the first note, while the ♯3 belongs with the note that coincides with the resolution of the suspension in a treble part. Many figures that signify resolution have thus been moved forward in this edition,[24] while a few figures have been moved backward.[25] A chord-player may choose, of course, to resolve any dissonance before or after a treble instrumentalist resolves it.

Dynamic Markings

The only dynamics engraved in the sources are Piano or Pia. and Forte or For. They have been reproduced in this edition as *piano* and *forte*. The only dynamic marking that is not found in all parts is the *forte* given for the violone in op. 1, no. 1.iii, measure 3, where it begins its constant eighth-note motion under a chain of suspensions.[26] In both sources, almost all the dynamic markings are found either at the end of the first half or the end of the movement. Most specify that the written-out reiteration of the final phrase must be played piano, as if it were an echo. In three sonatas, the echo in one movement is followed by a startling forte.[27] In *VI Sonate,* no. 4, at least one echo in *each* movement is followed by such a forte.[28] Piano echoes and forte shocks appear to be the bases for virtually all of the dynamics marked by Haym. Since he left most phrases unmarked, performers must themselves determine the dynamic levels for them.

In eighteen of the slow movements in this volume, the closing cadence on i/I is followed by a three-chord transition, consisting of V^6–iv^6–V in minor keys and V^6–vii^{o6}/V–V in major keys.[29] Nine in op. 1 and one in *VI Sonate* have quarter rests between the chords. They usually end movement 1, and their first chord is marked forte, while the next is marked piano.[30] The forte presumably serves as a jolt to warn listeners of the forthcoming change in tempo and mood. The remaining eight transitions, five in op. 1 and three in *VI Sonate,* usually end movement 3. They consist of sustained chords, without intervening rests, and should presumably be played piano throughout.[31]

Stems and Beams

Within the engraved prints, "modern" conventions already determined the direction of stems and—in most cases—the beaming of them. In the present edition, beams always encompass a dotted quarter note in $\frac{3}{8}$, $\frac{6}{8}$, and $\frac{12}{8}$, and a dotted half note in $\frac{6}{4}$. They usually encompass only a quarter note in ¢, C, and $\frac{3}{4}$, but four eighths that occur at the beginning or end of a ¢ or C measure are beamed together, as are six eighths that occur in $\frac{3}{4}$. In the engraved sources, such large groups of notes are frequently broken into smaller ones, which are easier to engrave when large leaps are present. Indeed, when engraved leaps of an octave were beamed, the upper note often had a downward stem, while the stem for the lower one pointed upwards. The relatively few alterations in beaming are not listed in the critical notes.

Accidentals

The engraved prints contain many cautionary accidentals.[32] For example, when any part leaps an augmented fourth or diminished fifth, one of the notes is usually preceded by a cautionary accidental, which "confirms" the rightness of the unusual interval.[33] Whenever a pitch that is preceded by a sharp, natural, or flat occurs two or more times within a measure, the accidental is repeated after any intervening note(s). Whenever a pitch recurs without such a cautionary accidental, the performer (and editor) should no longer observe the accidental.[34] Cautionary accidentals found in the sources are not reproduced in this edition, and their presence is not mentioned in the critical notes.

Tied Notes

The op. 1 partbooks contain many ties between pairs of notes that occur within the same measure. This is particularly true for violin 1, where the engraver seems to have visualized an imaginary barline in the middle of nearly every measure in **C** or ¢ time. Thus, a whole or a dotted half note at the beginning of a measure was written as a half tied to a half note or a half tied to a quarter note.[35] And a half or dotted quarter note that began on beat 2 was written as a quarter tied to a quarter or to an eighth note. Violin 2 also has such tied notes, especially when it intertwines with the first violin.[36] This is true even when one of the violins begins its notes on beats 1 and 3 and therefore does not cross an imaginary barline.[37] Perhaps Haym provided his engraver with a copy that was handwritten in this manner. It had great practical value in his age, when one staff often ended with the first half of a measure, and another began with the second half.[38] Such writing in "half-measure notation" may also help to explain the existence of cautionary accidentals, many of which occur after the partition of a measure in the middle.[39] The non-tied alternative, which utilizes dotted and undotted notes that bestride any imaginary barlines in the middle of measures, is also employed many times within op. 1.[40] In some passages, the engraver of op. 1 intermingled tied and dotted quarter notes occurring on beat 2.[41] This might signify that dotted notes were replacing tied ones. Indeed, the only such passage found in Haym's four sonatas within the *VI Sonate* employs dotted notes.[42] In the present edition, the "half-measure notation" has been replaced without report in the critical notes.

Critical Notes

The notes below list (1) rejected source readings, (2) Haym's ten handwritten additions in the GB-Lbl proofs, and (3) one handwritten addition found in the GB-Ob and GB-Och copies. Pitch names use the system in which middle C = c′. The following abbreviations are used: Vn. = Violin; Tr. = Transverse Flute, Oboe, or Violin; B. = Basso continuo part for Violone, Violoncello, Lute, or Cembalo.

Dodeci sonate a tre, Op. 1

Sonata No. 1 in D Minor

Adagio e Piano. M. 3, Vn. 2, note 1, forte added, then struck through in proof. M. 5, Vn. 1, note 2, half note.

Allegro. B. written in **C**. M. 10, B., note 2, figure ♯3. M. 12, Vn. 1, note 4, dotted quarter note.

Sonata No. 2 in F Major

Adagio. M. 12, B., note 1 (rather than 2) has piano.

Largo. M. 21, Vn. 2, piano added in proof.

Allegro. M. 11, B., note 1, dotted quarter note.

Sonata No. 3 in A Minor

Adagio. M. 10, Vns. 1 and 2, note 2, piano added in proofs.

Adagio. M. 2, B., note 1, half note. M. 2, Vn. 1, beat 3, fermata added in proof.

Vivace. M. 15, Vn. 1, note 1, dotted quarter note.

Sonata No. 4 in C Minor

Grave. M. 6, B., note 1, figure 6 (not 9).

Sonata No. 5 in G Major

Adagio. M. 3, Vn. 2, beat 4, fermata added in proof. M. 9, B., note 3, figure 9 (not 6). M. 22, Vn. 1, note 2, ♯ added in brown ink in GB-Ob and GB-Och copies.

Andante. M. 44, Vn. 1, note 3, half note.

Sonata No. 6 in C Major

Allegro. M. 23, Vn. 1, note 1, g′.

Sonata No. 8 in D Major

Gavotta. Vn. 1 written in **C**.

Sonata No. 9 in G Minor

Preludio. Mm. 2 and 5, Vn. 1, fermatas added in proof. M. 57, Vn. 1, note 1, something (= the replacement pitch f″?) added, then struck through in proof. M. 73, B. has a fermata (not present in the violin parts) placed over the rests.

Allemanda. M. 17, Vn. 2, note 4, eighth note.

Sonata No. 10 in E Minor

Preludio. M. 6, Vn. 1, note 4, quarter note.

Sonata No. 11 in A Major

Preludio. M. 5, Vn. 1, beat 4, fermata added in proof.

Sonata No. 12 in G Major

Preludio. M. 14, Vn. 2, note 1, whole note.

Giga. Mm. 15 and 38, Vn. 2, note 3, dotted quarter note.

From *VI Sonate da camera*

Sonata No. 1 in C Minor

Vivace. M. 10, B., note 1, figure 5.

Allegro. M. 21, Tr., note 1, quarter note. Mm. 21–26 written as three measures (with four beats per measure).

Sonata No. 2 in D Minor

Allegro. M. 11, the only rest is a sixteenth, written before the repeat sign.

Adagio. M. 15, Tr., note 1, c″.

Notes

1. *Complete Baronetage,* ed. G[eorge] E. C[okayne], 6 vols. (Exeter: William Pollard, 1900–1909), 1:36–37. According to Mr. Hopson, the baronetcy became extinct in 1972, when the sixteenth baronet died. I am grateful to Paul Atkin for sending me a photocopy of the bookplate.

2. According to Peter Ward-Jones, Music Librarian at the Bodleian, a previous owner may have written these numbers on the volumes.

3. In each case, the sharp is placed before the notehead, but is a half step above it.

4. I am grateful to John Milsom for examining the Christ Church records and sending me the date 1717. For information on the donor, see *The New Grove Dictionary of Music and Musicians,* 2d ed., s.v. "Aldrich, Henry," by Robert Shay, and see Henry Aldrich, *Selected Anthems and Motet Recompositions,* edited by Robert Shay, Recent Researches in the Music of the Baroque Era, vol. 85 (Madison: A-R Editions, 1998), vii–viii.

5. I am grateful to Charles Sens, Music Specialist at the Library of Congress, and to Anthony DelDonna for kindly describing and transcribing the particulars of this binding.

6. Two years after the publication of op. 1, an accurate reprint of the violin 1 part for no. 11.ii (Allemanda) was issued in *The Second Part of the Division Violin,* 4th ed. (London, [1705]), 37. This collection is no. 174 in William C. Smith, *A Bibliography of the Musical Works Published by John Walsh during the Years 1695–1720* (London: The Bibliographical Society, 1948; reprint, 1968), 55.

7. The print containing Haym and Bitti sonatas is the eleventh of nineteen listed in Roger's advertisement. Two Dutch guilders (= florins) were equivalent to four English shillings. I am grateful to Rudolf Rasch for supplying this information.

8. The librarian, Frohmut Dangel-Hofmann, has found such titles pasted on many volumes. She thus wonders whether the purchaser, Count Rudolf Franz Erwein von Schönborn, might have written them. I am grateful to Dr. Dangel-Hofmann for kindly supplying this and other information about the binding and condition of the score and cello part.

9. See Lindgren, "Count Rudolf Franz Erwein von Schönborn (1677–1754) and the Italian Sonatas for Violoncello in His Collection at Wiesentheid," in *Relazioni musicali tra Italia e Germania nell'età barocca, Atti del VI Convegno internazionale sulla musica italiana nei secoli XVII–XVIII, Loveno di Menaggio (Como), 11–13 July 1995,* ed. Alberto Colzani et al. (Como: Antiquae Musicae Italicae Studiosi and Centro italo-tedesco Villa Vigoni, 1997), 257–302.

10. Bononcini, *Musico prattico,* op. 8 (Bologna, 1673), 11; cf. William Klenz, *Giovanni Maria Bononcini of Modena: A Chapter in Baroque Instrumental Music* (Durham: Duke University Press, 1962), 57–58 and 116, and no. 63 in Smith, *A Bibliography of . . . the Years 1695–1720,* 22.

11. Lenton, *The Gentleman's Diversion, or The Violin Explained* (London, 1693), 6; since the only surviving copy of Lenton (in GB-CDp) lacks nearly all of its title page, the title has been derived from Michael Tilmouth, "A Calendar of References to Music in Newspapers Published in London and the Provinces (1660–1719)," *R. M. A. Research Chronicle* 1 (1961): 14.

12. John Playford, *An Introduction to the Skill of Music,* 12th ed., corrected and amended by Henry Purcell, facsimile edition, with a new introduction by Franklin B. Zimmerman (New York: Da Capo Press, 1972), 76.

13. Roger North, *On Music, being a Selection from His Essays Written during the Years c.1695–1728,* ed. John Wilson (London: Novello, 1959), 99–100, which is also printed in *Roger North's "The Musicall Grammarian 1728,"* ed. Mary Chan and Jamie C. Kassler (Cambridge: Cambridge University Press, 1990), 131.

14. Klenz, *Giovanni Maria Bononcini,* 59–61 and 116.

15. Lenton, *The Gentleman's Diversion,* 6. Purcell did not combine **C** with any triple-time signature in his 1694 edition of Playford's treatise.

16. No. 11.iv is also in $\frac{12}{8}$, but here the violone part is written in $\frac{12}{8}$, presumably because it occasionally subdivides the beats into quarter and eighth patterns.

17. In *VI Sonate,* no. 2.ii, for example, it could clarify eight hemiola cadences by combining mm. 9–10, 16–17, 19–20, 22–23, 26–27, 30–31, 33–34, and 36–37 into $\frac{3}{2}$ measures.

18. For examples, see op. 1, no. 4.iv in $\frac{6}{4}$, mm. 12–14 (cf. plate 4), and no. 5.iv in $\frac{6}{8}$, mm. 4, 6, 12, and 27.

19. Only the English signified a trill by means of a pair of diagonal lines. See North, *On Music . . . c.1695–1728,* 61–62, and Robert Donington, *The Interpretation of Early Music,* new rev. ed. (New York and London: W. W. Norton, 1992), 238, 242, 248, 258, and 262.

20. Examples for repetitions of dance strains are given in Robert E. Seletsky, "18th-Century Variations for Corelli's Sonatas, Op. 5," *Early Music* 24 (1996): 119–30. They are, of course, better suited to solo than to trio sonatas and more appropriate for chordal than for intricately contrapuntal textures. North's precepts pertaining to "the art of gracing" are given in North, *On Music . . . c.1695–1728,* 149–73.

21. Trills have been added in square brackets in no. 2.iv, mm. 38 and 40; no. 3.i, m. 5, and 3.iv, m. 48; no. 6.iv, m. 17; no. 7.i, m. 4, and 7.ii, mm. 16, 19, 33, and 36; no. 8.ii, m. 25, and 8.iv, mm. 16, 18, 20, and 30; no. 9.i, m. 60, and 9.ii, mm. 5, 7, and 12; no. 10.ii, m. 23, and 10.iv, m. 11; no. 11.ii, mm. 12, 19, and 20; and no. 12.ii, mm. 6 and 10. In some of these twenty-six examples, it is of course possible that Haym was merely denoting the presence of a cadence by means of its usual 4–3 figuration and was not calling for a dissonant 4.

22. Whenever a fermata is present in only one or two of the parts, it has been added in square brackets in the other(s). In the proofs for op. 1 at GB-Lbl, Haym made such corrections five times.

23. Perhaps such flourishes should resemble the florid stepwise "graces" added to adagios by Corelli for his op. 5 and by Babell for his two sets of *XII Solos.* Corelli's "graces" first appeared in a Roger edition of 1710: "Third Edition, which includes the *Adagio* embellishments for this work, composed by Mr. A. Corelli, as he plays them" (Troisieme Edition ou l'on a joint les agréemens des Adagio de cet ouvrage, composez par Mr. A. Corelli, comme il les joue). This edition was "pirated" by Walsh ca. 1711; see no. 400 in Smith, *A Bibliography of . . . the Years 1695–1720,* 120. Babell's two sets, which present the "proper Graces adapted to each Adagio by the Author," were printed by Walsh ca. 1725; see nos. 107 and 113 in William C. Smith and Charles Humphries, *A Bibliography of the Musical Works Published by the Firm of John Walsh during the Years 1721–1766* (London: The Bibliographical Society, 1968), 27 and 29. Roger must have correctly assigned the op. 5 embellishments to Corelli in 1710, because he and the maestro worked amicably in 1712, when they agreed on terms for publishing Corelli's op. 6. See Rudolf Rasch, "La famosa mano di Monsieur Roger: Antonio Vivaldi and His Dutch Publishers," *Informazioni e studi vivaldiani* 17 (1996): 89–135, esp. 131 n. 4; Rasch, "Corelli's Contract: Notes on the Publication History of the *Concerti grossi . . . Opera sesta* [1714]," *Tijdschrift van de Koninklijke Vereniging voor Nederlandse Muziekgeschiedenis* 46 (1996): 83–135; Neal Zaslaw, "Ornaments for Corelli's Violin Sonatas, Op. 5," *Early Music* 24 (1996): 102–4; and Peter Allsop, *Arcangelo Corelli: New Orpheus of Our Times* (Oxford: Oxford University Press, 1999), 135–37. See also Hans Joachim Marx, "Some Unknown Embellishments of Corelli's Violin Sonatas," *Musical*

Quarterly 61 (1975): 65–76, and Charles Gower Price, "Free Ornamentation in the Solo Sonatas of William Babell: Defining a Personal Style of Improvised Embellishment," *Early Music* 29 (2001): 29–54.

24. An example is the 6–5 suspension in op. 1, no. 7.i, m. 13, beat 1, and its echo in m. 15, beat 3. In the engraved print, the 6 and 5 are both placed over the half note, while in this edition the 5 has been moved to the ensuing quarter note.

25. An example is the 4–♭3 suspension in no. 4.iv, m. 33. In the engraved print, the ♭3 resolution is placed directly above the second bass note in the measure, while in this edition it has been moved back to where the first violin provides it.

26. In the proofs for violin 2 at GB-Lbl, Haym added "forte" under note 1 in m. 3, then crossed it out. This confirms that only the violone should play forte in this passage.

27. Op. 1, no. 2.iv, m. 39; op. 1, no. 10.iii, m. 11; and *VI Sonate,* no. 3.iv, m. 28 (which leads to a quasi-echo in m. 30).

28. No. 4.i, m. 17; 4.ii, mm. 11, 27, and 39; 4.iii, m. 29; and 4.iv, mm. 16 and 54.

29. One of the eighteen, op. 1, no. 2.i, includes four chords: V^6–I–vii$^{\circ 6}$/V–V.

30. In op. 1, the nine movements with such dynamic markings for detached-chord transitions are nos. 1.iii, 2.i, 3.i, 5.i, 6.i, 6.iii, 11.i, 11.iii, and 12.i. The similar movement in *VI Sonate,* which has no dynamic markings, is no. 1.i, which is shown on plate 4.

31. They are op. 1, nos. 1.i, 4.iii, 8.iii, 9.iii, and 12.iii, and *VI Sonate,* nos. 1.iii, 2.iii, and 3.iii. Note that op. 1, no. 12.iii, does have forte and piano markings, and that *VI Sonate,* no. 1.iii, has a forte marking. Note that a forte marking is likewise given for similar iv^6–V transitions after a full cadence at the mid-point of *VI Sonate,* no. 4.ii, m. 11, and no. 4.iv, m. 16, both of which are fast movements.

32. They also contain an accidental before or above the *mostra* at the end of a staff whenever the note that begins the next staff is preceded by an accidental. This is true of Haym's opp. 1–2, his editions of Corelli's opp. 1–5, and the *VI Sonate.* For a definition of *mostra,* which is equivalent to the Latin *index* and French *guidon,* see *A Short Explication of Such Foreign Words as are made use of in Musick Books* (London: J[ohn] Brotherton, 1724), 39. According to Lenton, *The Gentleman's Diversion,* p. 6, and Playford, *An Introduction to the Skill of Musick,* 78, the English called it a "Direct."

33. Some of these accidentals have been preserved in this edition. See, for example, the violone in op. 1, no. 2.ii, m. 16, note 3; and violin 2 in no. 3.iii, m. 4, note 4; no. 4.ii, m. 10, note 1; no. 4.iii, m. 6, note 2; and no. 7.iii, m. 11, note 3. Two examples of such leaps that have no cautionary accidental in the engraved source are in no. 7.iii, violin 2, m. 2, note 7, and m. 5, note 2.

34. For examples, see violin 2 in op. 1, no. 7.iv, m. 14, note 5; violin 1 in no. 9.ii, m. 12, note 9, and no. 12.ii, m. 10, note 9; and the treble part in *VI Sonate,* no. 3.i, m. 19, note 7.

35. Examples are found in no. 2.i, m. 8; no. 3.i, mm. 1–2; no. 3.ii, mm. 5, 29, and 34–35; no. 3.iii, m. 6; and no. 4.iv, m. 40. Examples are also found in the violin 2 partbook, as in no. 4.iv, mm. 33 and 35.

36. See, for example, violin 2 in no. 6.i, mm. 3, 8, 14, 17, and 19, and no. 6.ii, mm. 7, 13, 14, 16, 18, 21, and 38.

37. See, for example, no. 1.ii, where violin 1 in mm. 4, 6, 17, 20, 26, 29–30, 34, 43, and 45 intertwines with violin 2, which plays it in mm. 17–18, 20, and 29–30. Similar passages are found in three slow movements: no. 5.i, mm. 8 and 16–18; no. 8.i, mm. 12–13; and no. 9.iii, mm. 5–7.

38. See, for example, violin 1 in no. 1.ii, m. 17, and no. 6.ii, mm. 2 and 26; violin 2 in no. 7.i, m. 10, no. 7.iv, m. 7, and no. 9.ii, mm. 10 and 15; and violone in no. 6.i, m. 12. They all have a tie between the half-measure at the end of one staff and the half-measure at the beginning of the next.

39. For example, see *VI Sonate,* no. 1.i, m. 9, beat 3 in the bass, which is preceded by a natural sign (as shown on plate 4), and no. 1.ii, m. 14, beat 3 in the treble, which is preceded by a flat.

40. See, for example, the half notes on beat 2 in violin 2 for no. 1.i, mm. 2, 5, and 15; no. 1.ii, mm. 7, 12, and 14; no. 2.ii, mm. 14–17 and 23–27; no. 5.i, mm. 9 and 20; and no. 5.ii, mm. 28 and 33.

41. In the engraved print, the quarter note on the second beat in violin 1 is dotted in no. 8.i, m. 12, but tied to an eighth in m. 13. It is similarly dotted in no. 9.iii, mm. 5–6, but tied in m. 7; tied in no. 10.iii, mm. 6–7, but dotted in mm. 9–10 (the echo!); tied in no. 11.i, m. 1 and its repetition in m. 13, but dotted in m. 2 and its repetition in m. 14. In violin 2, the second beat is tied in no. 12.i, m. 10, but dotted in m. 11.

42. No. 4.i, treble, mm. 3–6.